Getting To
The Heart
Of The Platter

30 Words To Weigh Less

And Give You Something Else To Chew On
So Pounds Come Off For Good!

by Cynthia Magg

TranscendingMindset.com
P.O. Box 620682
Woodside, CA 94062

Getting To The Heart Of The Platter
Copyright © 2013 by Cynthia Magg

Edited by
Christina M. Alex and Rebecca Ortese

ISBN—978-0-988-5207-7-6

My Struggle With Weight

Like many women, I have been dieting on and off for more than 30 years, and it has been exhausting!

I reached my lowest weight of 113 when I swam competitively in high school and did not consume enough calories for my level of sports activity. Yet there was a deeper reason for my becoming so dangerously thin—my living environment had not been safe. In childhood, punishments were handed out at the end of a leather belt, and worse, molestation was allowed to occur. Ashamed of and disconnected from my body in a multitude of ways, I was so unhappy that I tried to disappear off the face of the planet by slowly starving myself.

I gained the most weight during my 4 years of college. To escape my life, I filled myself by binge drinking and eating whenever and whatever I wanted (oftentimes indulging in Captain Crunch cereal for breakfast, lunch, and dinner). Come graduation time, I was still unhappy and unprepared to handle the stresses of the real world.

Initially, I chose to follow a traditional corporate America career path. Yet after 10 years of only filling up my bank account, I became a pastry chef, so I could be surrounded by sweetness and feed those parts of my body and spirit that were unfulfilled and starving for love, attention, and kindness. However, this new road paved with sweetness had other things in store for me— one of which was to lead me to a career in holistic healing, so I could finally face up to my own health issues.

For most of my adult life, my weight has fluctuated up or down 10-20 pounds. I quickly discovered that a few pounds in either direction determined whether my clothes fit. Hence, over the years, I tried a whole host of diets and learned that most of them work, provided that I committed to staying on them for the rest of my life. And while I now enjoy exercising, for most of my life I worked out because I hated parts of myself and my body. I only began to stop that cycle when I discovered the trigger words that were lying at the bottom of my damaged spirit. I share these with you in the following pages.

Throughout my life, I've come to realize that I am a work in progress and parts of me are coming alive after being dormant for so many years. Now in my late 40's, I am not on a diet and I prefer to move my body through dancing or hiking...any activity that is not forced, allows me to go at my own pace, or be out in nature. Currently, I have stabilized at the lowest, healthiest weight I've ever known in over 30 years.

I have lived every chapter of this book. And, since life operates on its own terms, I ended up reliving them as I wrote.

This book was birthed from the work that I do with clients who are in physical and emotional pain, since excess weight is a manifestation of the emotional burdens we all carry. I hope my work can help anyone who struggles with their weight to heal their body and soul.

~Cynthia Magg

Dedicated to every woman
who's ever been on a diet, lost weight,
and gained it all back...and then some.

Ladies, it's time the 'Pounds Come Off For Good!'

S.O.S.

A message for <u>you</u> from your inner child

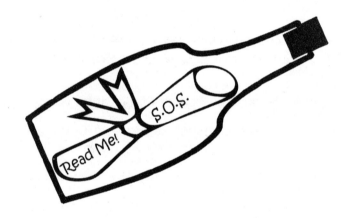

Hello You,

Should you choose to go on a **diet**, you will face every "**why bother**" excuse possible. You then reflect on your self-**worth** and vow to **succeed** this time and not **fail** again. Yet, you can't seem to shake the **pain** and despair that washes over you as you wonder if depriving yourself for the rest of your life is worth it to be one of the **thin people**. You **control** and swallow an urge to scream and stuff down the **anger** that arises every time you think about dieting.

Overwhelmed by the mere thought of one more letdown in your life and starving for just a little **attention**, you may be wishing someone would unconditionally **support** you in the ways you want and need. When you choose to diet, you could really benefit from some **acceptance** and a little TLC (Tender Loving Care), especially from your **family**. Yet creating healthier **boundaries** with them, other people, or food often seems as **hopeless** as reaching your weight loss goals. Feeling **depressed** and **frustrated** just makes you feel more **stuck** (usually before your diet's even begun).

Sweetness, as far as you can remember, only comes in wrapped packages. And the **easiness** and speed at which you can indulge in your beloved favorite foods when unwanted emotions get triggered concerns you since you can devour and gorge weigh beyond **fullness**. You **love** the **enjoyment** these pleasurable foods bring, yet not the effect they have on your expanding waistline. And if the thought of **letting go** of them once again is agonizing, how are you to make it through your stress-filled days or be able to handle anxiety-rich **social eating** scenarios if you won't be able to **treat** yourself? To boot, you may already feel heavy with **guilt**, worrying that you might cheat on your diet. If you stopped putting **others first**, then you could devote more time to your health and well-being which would help resolve your weight issues sooner. ☺

With love,
Your Inner Child

WHAT'S ON THE MENU/TABLE OF CONTENTS

"What you seek is seeking you."
~Rumi

Welcome

To the Women's Edition of
'Getting To The Heart Of The Platter'!

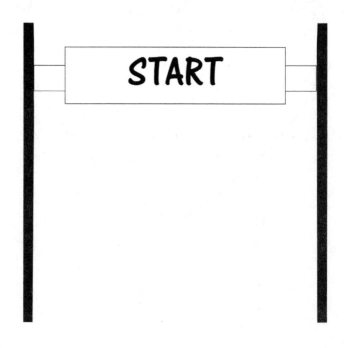

START

A few things to help make <u>Your Weight Loss Journey</u> easier for you:

- <u>Read a chapter a day. (Or, go at your own pace).</u>
  A chapter a day can help you to safely shed unwanted pounds more easily. Yet, as there is a lot to chew on in each chapter, give yourself the time you need to digest it. You get to choose the speed at which you want to devour this book.

- <u>Trust your inner guidance</u>.
  This journey is not about you powering through to the finish line. Instead, it's about giving yourself permission to reconnect with and listen to your intuition—which you often did as a young girl.

- <u>Use your imagination creatively</u>.
  Take the time at the end of each chapter to do the exercises in the journal section because these are the tools that will accelerate your results. When doing the exercises, write down what first comes to mind; and if nothing comes to mind, allow your inner child to use her imagination creatively.

- <u>Check out the resources</u>.
  In the appendices, you'll find a sample list of both positive and negative feelings that you can refer to when doing the exercises in chapters 2 (Diet) and 19 (Frustrated), pages 213 and 215 respectively. Plus, you'll also find information about using our online support to accompany you on your weight loss journey on page 217.

- <u>Enroll a friend</u>.
  Any journey can be made more enjoyable with a friend, especially if you really like the company! It's a great way to start to build a weight loss support network. Plus, what better place to start that team than with a close friend.

- <u>Be gentle with yourself</u>.

  Your relationship with food is sacred to you. Food provides nourishment, comfort, stress-relief, enjoyment, and celebration—just to name a few. Food has fed your amazing body, yet it cannot feed your amazing soul. Having chosen to read this book, you know that part of you is ready to discover and examine what you may truly be starving for.

When you start on your journey to shift and rebalance your relationship with food, you naturally give yourself permission to get your dream body back and to maintain it with ease. ☺

Blessings to you as you embark on your journey!

As you set out on
Your Weight Loss Discovery Journey, know that...

'There is a life-force within your soul, seek that life.
There is <u>a gem</u> in the mountain of your body, seek that mine.
O traveler, if you are in search of That
Don't look outside, <u>look inside yourself</u> and seek That.'
~Rumi

1

<u>SHOULD</u>

My Way Or The Highway

As we grow up, we are all made to travel a never-ending road of rules, restrictions, and conditions—SHOULDS—that can make us feel obligated, constrained, and deprived.

Some of these SHOULDS are common sense, like looking both ways before crossing the street or obeying traffic signs. However, most of the SHOULDs that run through our minds have been imposed by others and, let's face it, no one likes to be told what to do.

Yet since early childhood, other people (parents, other family members, teachers, authority figures, bosses, friends, spouses, significant others) have been doing just that—telling you what you SHOULD or SHOULDN'T do.

Many of those people mean well and believe that they know better or what is truly best. Yet, they may also be trying to get their own wants and needs met through telling you what to do. And failure to stay within the yellow lines of their 'My Way or the Highway' behavior control can lead you to a life of frustration and self-defeat.

For example, feeling conflicted between doing what you SHOULD versus doing what you WANT can lead you to rebel and sabotage your own efforts to succeed. This can be true, especially when it comes to dieting and losing weight.

For many people, childhood mealtimes were a fertile ground for a lot of SHOULDs that were dished out and tied to the power struggles they had with adults. Though most food experiences and mealtimes are remembered with love, attention, nurturing, and nutrition, many are linked with punishment, deprivation, and shame. You may have been forced to do and to eat a lot of things you didn't want to; and any attempts to rebel against the hand that fed you may have led to a variety of punishments, including being starved.

To say the least, many people do not know how to identify, let alone evolve the conflicting feelings, emotions, and memories they have towards food—all of which further stalls their weight loss efforts.

Until now.

This Weight Loss Discovery Journey will be a powerful aid for you to identify and examine the things you think you SHOULD do related to dieting, weight loss, and food in general. This will allow you to begin to shift and rebalance the power struggles you experienced in childhood and which you may now be experiencing as an adult. It will also allow you to finally give your inner child the freedom to choose her own path, even if that path is currently unknown.

Your Weight Loss Discovery Journey begins now!

<u>Your Weight Loss Discovery Journal</u>: SHOULD

For the following journal opportunities, write down what first comes to mind. And if nothing comes to mind, allow your inner child to use her imagination creatively.

1. Write down everything you've been told you SHOULD or SHOULDN'T do to lose weight.

EXAMPLE: To lose weight, I SHOULD/SHOULDN'T...

2. Write down everything you WANT to be able to do while you are losing weight.

EXAMPLE: While losing weight, I WANT to honor, nourish, and take care of myself by...

2
DIET

Eat Like A Bird

When you think about a new diet or even just watching what you eat, many memories will probably flood your mind of all the diets you've ever been on that didn't work.

These memories may still be haunting and taunting you.

Suddenly making any kind of dietary change may feel more like being stuck on a Dessertless Island Eating Twigs and other vegetation, all of which sounds about as appealing as eating like a bird.

You may have also experienced diets that are not much fun, that are a lot of hard work, and that are full of emotional pain such as:

Deprivation
Isolation
Exhaustion
Tension
Struggle

Every diet on the planet requires you to muster up your willpower, to be hyper-vigilant around food, and to rigidly follow all of the rules of the plan in order to achieve the results that are promised.

On a diet, you'll:

- Do things you don't really want to do
- Give up things you like
- Eat things you don't like
- Adhere to someone else's way of eating
- Never experience the fulfillment of discovering healthy eating your way

Adhering to the restrictions of a diet without being on a Weight Loss Discovery Journey will almost guarantee your inner child will immediately surface with the shout, 'You CAN'T make me!' And once your inner child feels discounted or ignored, she may very well sabotage your efforts to lose weight in a variety of ways. With so much weighing against your good intentions, you may find yourself wondering, 'What Does It Ever Take to lose weight and keep the pounds off for good?'

If only losing weight were as simple as some people make it sound:

DIET = Eat Less + Exercise More = Less Calories In + More Calories Burned = Weigh Less

You may give that old weight loss formula a go for a while, and when it doesn't work, you may give the newest diet math a try and count calories, add up points, select from a rainbow of colors, or measure out serving sizes.

And there you are, going from one diet to the next, always hoping to find the right formula. Yet no matter how diet math adds up, the weight may not budge or budge quickly enough.

And if you've read this far, you are becoming aware that other factors weigh in that cannot be measured on the scale. These factors are the biggest reasons why the diet math does not always compute and why following one diet after another may be a heck of a lot easier than taking a deeper look at all of the other weighty issues that you carry around within you.

The only thing known for sure about adhering to the diet math is that it still means having to sacrifice beloved favorite foods that comfort, soothe, and provide enjoyment.

This equates to:

D   **D**isappointments
I   =   **I**'ll
E   **E**xperience
T   **T**oday

Take a moment now to reflect on what 'dieting' requires you to give up.

This type of reflection can make it easier to avoid triggering your inner child and sabotaging your weight loss efforts, so that whether you choose to diet or not, you will be able to tune into the knowledge of your inner self. To discover what needs to happen for you to lose weight, it's necessary for you to awaken and listen to the parts of yourself that may be hidden and hurting. This in turn can help you to align your heart with your weight loss goals and help to reveal a healthier and more slender version of you that lies just beneath the surface.

Your Weight Loss Discovery Journal: DIET

For the following journal opportunities, write down what first comes to mind. And if nothing comes to mind, allow your inner child to use her imagination creatively.

1. Write down the foods, beverages, and other things that you like that you will have to restrict or give up when you go on a diet.

EXAMPLE: I don't like diets because I will have to restrict or give up the following foods, beverages, or other things...

2. Write down how you WANT to feel in your body while you are trying to lose weight.

(For a sample list of positive feelings, go to the Appendix on page 213. Or, go to: http://gtthotp.com/handouts/gtthotp%20positive.pdf)

EXAMPLE: While losing weight, I WANT to feel...

3
<u>WHY BOTHER</u>
Will It Bear Fruit?

On days when you feel frustrated and fed up, a 'Why Bother' frame of mind begins to sprout. It then takes root to hamper your growth, especially when you are trying something new. Doubts fuel underlying skepticism. Resistance makes you question your efforts. And loss of faith sabotages your ability to believe that Your Weight Loss Discovery Journey will ever bear fruit.

When 'Why Bother' thoughts start growing, your mind will inevitably sow variations of 'It'll never work for me':

- It's never worked before
- I've tried so many times
- It'll take too long
- It costs too much money
- Nothing really changes
- I'll never be able to learn to do it anyway
- That's just the way I am
- That's just the way it is
- I'll just have to live with it

You may try to convince yourself that these are valid reasons not to make the effort. Why go through all the trouble? Why take the pain? Why put yourself out? Why keep at it? Why not just stick with what you already know? Sure it feels safe, yet it has never given you what you want.

These 'Why Bother' thoughts may be further complicated by the fact that someone else may have told you that you SHOULD do this/try this/read this/buy that. And some part of you may give up on Your Weight Loss Discovery Journey just because someone else told you to do it.

'Why bother' is a subtle form of resistance. And like almost all forms of resistance, some part of yourself is trying to protect you from any potential pain or disappointment you may experience on your journey to your goals.

Identifying how this 'Why Bother' frame of mind may be controlling and limiting your efforts to succeed at losing weight can help you let go of this kind of resistance.

After all, what else have you got to lose?

For the following journal opportunities, write down what first comes to mind. And if nothing comes to mind, allow your inner child to use her imagination creatively.

1. Take a moment to think about everything that you've tried in the past to lose weight that didn't work: diets, products, gadgets, equipment, gear, foods, beverages, supplements, pills, books, DVDs, coaching, etc.

Then, write down any skeptical or resistant thoughts that come to mind when you think about doing something new to lose weight.

EXAMPLE: I have the following skeptical or resistant thoughts about trying something new:

2. Write down what you hope a new approach will do for you.

EXAMPLE: By trying something new, I WANT it to...

4

<u>WORTH</u>

Worth Your Weight In Gold

Congratulations. You are getting there!

And as you identify your remaining resistant 'Why Bother' thoughts, you may continue to wonder whether your efforts to lose weight will be:

- Worth your time of day
- Worth the sacrifices
- Worth waiting for

Will you ever fully achieve your desired weight loss? That is the question.

And, underneath all of your doubts lurk the core issues:

1) Do you feel worthy of having the body you desire?
2) Do you feel you deserve to get what you want?

The answers reside just below the surface where your dieting and weight loss resistance has its roots—in your feelings of self-worth.

Your current feelings of self-worth (i.e. how you judge and weigh yourself) probably hinge upon how others have measured your worth on the scale of life. In the 'Good—Better—Best' ranking comparison systems within families, schools, and at work, you formed certain beliefs about your value. These beliefs develop with the amount and quality of time others spent with you and if they made you feel acknowledged, accepted, adored, and loved—or not.

If you felt others held you in high esteem or regard (especially your parents), you were made to feel good and praiseworthy which helped to fill you up on an energetic and emotional level.

Yet, if you were made to feel invalidated or that you truly didn't matter, you probably felt bad and blameworthy/shameworthy, causing a feeling of emptiness inside—an emptiness which carries its own kind of heaviness in your heart and soul.

As a further burden, your already emotionally-charged feelings of worth can be intensified by other unresolved and disappointing emotional events that have happened throughout your lifetime. Many of these events occurred when you were young, at a time when you had little or no control over your life. If you were never given support to help you heal from those events, you found ways to survive them. And since children often zealously believe that whatever happens is their fault, you may have tried to rationalize in your mind that if you were simply 'Worthy Enough', then only good things would happen to you.

Not measuring up in the eyes of loved ones, nor successfully meeting the expectations of others, goes to the very core of this program.

When you feel 'Not Worthy Enough' of anyone's time, love, and attention, you may attempt to earn love and attention through accomplishments and goals. This can include your weight loss goals, especially if your hurt inner child believes that you will continue to be 'Not Worthy Enough' until you lose the weight or get 'Thin Enough'.

However, you know there is no guarantee that reaching your weight loss goal will ever make you 'Worthy Enough' in the eyes of another. That's when your 'Why Bother' thoughts can push up from underground and sabotage your efforts. And while this may ultimately hurt you, it also keeps you safe by maintaining a predictable status quo. For that is often the price you may think you need to pay to keep peace in your life, especially with family members and significant others who may be threatened by the power of your success.

Before you ever physically step on a scale to weigh your body, it's important to begin to reflect on how 'Not Worthy Enough' has woven itself into your life, especially if you notice that you have a tendency to derail yourself. 'Not Worthy Enough' shows up as self-criticism and spending endless hours doubting your abilities.

If any of this is true for you, give yourself permission to shift your mindset. Shower your inner child with the respect and honor she deserves. Free yourself. Free your energy. Nourish yourself in new ways. Begin to see yourself through a new set of eyes. Follow your heart all the way to achieving your weight loss goals.

Your Weight Loss Discovery Journal: WORTH

For the following journal opportunities, write down what first comes to mind. And if nothing comes to mind, allow your inner child to use her imagination creatively.

1. What did you never get enough of growing up?

EXAMPLE: Growing up, I feel I never got enough...

2. List 3 (or more) things that others praise and acknowledge you for.

EXAMPLE: Others praise and acknowledge me for the following things...

5

SUCCEED

At What Price?

Success has the potential to attract the positive—as well as the negative—into your life. So when it comes to setting and achieving goals, your thoughts about success can make you feel a range of emotions, from being excited and hopeful all the way to being nervous and afraid.

You get excited because you've imagined all of the ways your life will change for the better. Additionally, when you envision reaching your goal, this excitement helps to keep you motivated on your journey. Yet the fearful parts of you may not feel you deserve success since you may still believe you have endless work to do to prove your 'Worthiness' to others.

What's more, you may doubt whether successfully reaching your goal will make you feel as you hoped or imagined it would. You may also have preconceived beliefs from your youth about the qualities, traits, and attitudes a person who succeeds must have. Other parts of you may be concerned about the possible changes that success will bring to your life and all of your interpersonal relationships, especially if you fear you could lose friends or feel embarrassed about your success.

Success comes at a price. Or so you've been told.

That price may be making choices and sacrifices to get something you want. Yet, if you feel forced to give up something you truly want or are not ready to let go, you may sabotage your efforts. With weight loss, if you end up feeling like you are losing in every other part of your life except when you step on the scale, is it worth it?

It's pretty safe to say that we'd all prefer to enjoy the sweet smell of success and avoid failure altogether. Most of us fear success as much as we fear failure*, so it's to your advantage to address both fears. This chapter helps you to begin to identify your fear of successfully reaching your weight loss goals.

*FYI...the next chapter addresses the fear of failure.

Your Weight Loss Discovery Journal: SUCCEED

For the following journal opportunities, write down what first comes to mind. And if nothing comes to mind, allow your inner child to use her imagination creatively.

1. Write down any negative things that could happen to you while you lose weight.

Include any worries and fears, as well as any unwanted sacrifices, and how you believe losing weight could negatively affect your interpersonal relationships with your parents, spouse/significant other, siblings, co-workers, friends, etc.

EXAMPLE: The following negative things could happen while I lose weight...

2. Write down any positive things that could happen to you while you lose weight.

Include any hopes and dreams, as well as how things would change for the better, and how you believe losing weight could positively affect your interpersonal relationships with your parents, spouse/significant other, siblings, co-workers, friends, etc.

EXAMPLE: The following positive things could happen while I lose weight...

6
<u>FAIL</u>

Bow Your Head In Shame

We have all experienced the pain, as well as the fear, of failure. Everyone has failed. Yet, nobody really wants to fail at anything. Even if failing is part of the learning process in life, we don't like how others make us feel ashamed when we do. And we don't like the fact that some people in our lives need to keep painfully reminding us of our prior failures to make themselves feel more successful.

Early on in life, you fearlessly tried new things all the time with no real thought as to whether you would succeed. It was all fun and games. Then you learned the value of winning and losing, winners and losers, and success and failure. You also learned that success is celebrated and failure is frowned upon.

Failure meant that you came up short, were lacking in something, or didn't meet the expectations of others. You may have disappointed someone or let others down. To say the least, failure quickly earned a bad name, and you became cautious and fearful. In the present, your fear of failure rises to the surface as you attempt to lose weight, exhausting yourself in the process.

Your failure to reach your weight loss goals can sometimes feel more hopeless than you can bear. Plus, it can energetically keep you weighed down. You can unknowingly carry your failures forward with you and easily fall into the 'Why Bother' frame of mind. This often makes setting new goals a bigger challenge than it needs to be. It can also feed your feelings of being 'Not Worthy Enough'.

When you use this program to identify and address the core issues preventing you from achieving success, you will triumph over past failures and steer clear of resistance and self-sabotage.

As mentioned in the previous chapter, failure, like success, has the potential to bring both the positive and the negative into your life. Therefore, when fear of failure begins to surface in your mind, beginning to identify its possible hold over you allows you to keep your head held high throughout your weight loss journey.

<u>Your Weight Loss Discovery Journal</u>: FAIL

For the following journal opportunities, write down what first comes to mind. And if nothing comes to mind, allow your inner child to use her imagination creatively.

1. Write down anything negative that could happen to you if you don't lose weight.

Include any worries and fears and how you believe that not losing weight could negatively impact your interpersonal relationships with your parents, siblings, spouse/significant other, co-workers, friends, etc.

EXAMPLE: The following negative things could happen if I don't lose weight...

2. Write down anything positive that could happen to you if you don't lose weight.

Include how you believe that not losing weight could positively impact your interpersonal relationships with your parents, siblings, spouse/significant other, co-workers, friends, etc.

EXAMPLE: The following positive things could happen if I don't lose weight...

7

PAIN

Breaks Your Heart

We all hate pain—physical or emotional—and will do all sorts of things to avoid it. To escape pain—real or imagined—you might engage in behavior or make choices that sabotage your efforts to reach your weight loss goals. And while your physical pains seem to heal a lot quicker than your emotional pains, both leave the body and soul torn and tattered, with a few scars—though not all injuries are visible to the human eye.

Pain breaks your heart and causes it to ache. It leads to immense suffering and grief. And when you are hurt, you might say 'Never again' and silently slip a protective coating around your heart. This energetic protective barrier prevents further injury from piercing and penetrating the depths of your being. Pain then feels like a death, since your core becomes closed off and shut down. And still, you put on a smile and pretend you're not hurting inside. Or, you might transfer your pain onto others, mostly in unconscious ways; because after all, misery loves company.

As a small child, you hopefully had caregivers who offered comfort until physical hurts and emotional pains went away. Sometimes all it took was a band-aid and a kiss to make you feel better. A treat or a favorite food may have been given to stop any crying, as a way to comfort you when you were sick, or to sugarcoat a visit to the doctor's office—all unknowingly kick-starting a habitual use of food as pain reliever.

When you were young, someone may have always been around to help distract you from your pain. Now, when pain surfaces in your body, you probably reach for the quickest way to get rapid relief from that pain, especially if there is no one around to distract you from it. We turn to comfort foods, OTC drugs, and other serious pain-numbing substances, habits, and addictions.

These temporary solutions become ineffective as the body becomes acclimated to whatever substance you might choose; over time you must consume larger quantities or stronger doses to keep old pains stuffed down and new ones from surfacing. You push healing away every time you avoid addressing your core issues and the deeper hurts inside your heart. This, in turn, pushes your weight loss goals further out of reach.

We all shut down whenever we are in pain, and we all need time to heal from those injuries. Yet, spending years reliving painful moments is not the best use of your amazing body or incredible mind.

Pain may be easily triggered and feel quite sacred to you. It can even become an essential and defining part of your identity. Families and loved-ones often know your pain, because they may be the ones who inflicted the initial hurts and disappointments. You may now be unconsciously holding on to your pain, letting the physical weight you carry on your body physically represent that pain as you wait/weight for the person who inflicted it on you to finally apologize—even if that person is no longer in your life or even living. You may also be attached to your pain through the story you tell yourself (and others) about your life. If you let the pain go, who would you be? How would your life change if you didn't use your pain as an excuse?

Being on a diet and losing weight can be physically and emotionally painful for you, reminding you of the deprivation and frustration you may have felt as a child. You may experience the gamut from hunger pangs to exercise-induced muscle pains to the embarrassment of letting others see your body when you undress in the locker room.

So here you are again, following someone else's specific diet plan where you must commit to their rules to get the results you are promised. This experience could trigger memories of other disappointments and unkept promises, as if this time this diet will lead you to fulfillment and wipe the old slate clean. In the meantime, you may only be punishing yourself just to meet someone else's standards.

Being on a Diet = Being in Pain

Diets are long and painful, requiring you to stomach the pain, put in the effort, and punish yourself by going without your favorite foods.

Man cannot live on bread alone, yet you may be using bread and/or its other food equivalents to make up for the lack of time, love, and attention from others. Your remarkable inner child is willing to take the self-inflicted pain of being on a diet in order to be thin and loveable. You hurt yourself—through starving and depriving your body—to prevent someone else from judging or hurting you. Yet what you are truly starving for is tender loving care, which feeds your heart and soul and helps you heal at the deepest level. Only you, yourself, can provide that to you, yourself—until you feel safe enough to let someone else into your heart again.

Before you choose to take another trip down the dieting highway, you are encouraged to use this Weight Loss Discovery Journey to shed some light on how your inner child tries to protect you from pain by comforting you with food.

Your Weight Loss Discovery Journal: PAIN

For the following journal opportunities, write down what first comes to mind. And if nothing comes to mind, allow your inner child to use her imagination creatively.

1. What do you believe you would need to do to protect yourself from ever experiencing physical or emotional pain of any kind ever again?

EXAMPLE: To protect myself from ever experiencing physical or emotional pain of any kind in my body I would need to...

2. List 3 (or more) non-food related things that comfort you and make you feel relaxed and safe.

EXAMPLE: The following things comfort me and make me feel relaxed and safe...

8

<u>THIN PEOPLE</u>

A Strong Wind Could Blow You Away

(Feel free to replace 'thin' with slender, skinny, slim, slight, lean, small...whatever words resonate the most with you.)

When you are trying to lose weight, your opinion about thin people or people that weigh less than you truly matters and can be a determining factor in just how long you will stay on your weight loss journey. Plus, how you feel others in your life will view and treat a thinner version of your current self contributes to how much weight you will allow yourself to lose. Additionally, what size other members of your family are in comparison to you is of importance and carries some weight—pun intended. ☺

Many people may feel threatened by your desire to change. Someone in your family or social network may become jealous if you lose weight, regardless of their current shape or size, especially if they feel it will take attention away from them. Your desire to lose weight and be thinner sends all sorts of messages to others in your life who may unconsciously attempt to sabotage you to get their own needs met first.

You probably perceive thin people in positive and negative ways. Positive in the sense that you believe and imagine that being thin can bring pluses and benefits into your life. Yet, if at the same time you view thin people as weak, invisible, vulnerable, unprotected, frail, able to be easily hurt or insulted, and/or lacking strength, then some part of you will keep the weight on to protect you and keep you safe from harm, pain, or injury of any kind—real or imagined.

You may also view a thin person as always having to be on a diet to stay thin, and just thinking about that can seem like a lot of work and deprivation or too high of a price to pay. Not to mention how our society still equates thin with beauty, at least for women. Yet, what thin means to you and what you think in your mind is what truly matters the most. Take anorexic people, for example—almost everyone else can see that they are severely underweight, yet most anorexics still see themselves as being fat or overweight.

To let go of any fears and concerns and get out of this weight loss jam or dieter's dilemma, it's important to clear from your body and mind what you perceive to be the negatives about losing weight or becoming thin. Doing so will help you stay grounded as well as prevent you from sabotaging your efforts to successfully lose weight.

Your Weight Loss Discovery Journal: THIN PEOPLE

For the following journal opportunities, write down what first comes to mind. And if nothing comes to mind, allow your inner child to use her imagination creatively.

1. Write down anything you think of as a negative or potential drawback to losing weight or becoming a thinner version of your current self.

Include any worries, fears, and beliefs about how being thinner could negatively impact your interpersonal relationships with your parents, siblings, spouse/significant other, possible romantic partners, co-workers, friends, etc.

EXAMPLE: The negatives or potential drawbacks to becoming thin or thinner are...

2. Write down anything you think of as a positive or a potential benefit to losing weight or becoming a thinner version of yourself.

Include any hopes and dreams and how you believe being thinner could positively impact your interpersonal relationships with your parents, siblings, spouse/significant other, possible romantic partners, co-workers, friends, etc.

EXAMPLE: The positives or potential benefits to becoming thin or thinner are...

9

CONTROL

Know Limits

You truly become a glutton for punishment every time you take on the pain of being on a diet, any diet, without investigating what has lead to your issues with weight in the first place.

Diets are about controlling yourself, staying inside the yellow lines, and KNOWING your limits vs. being out of control, stepping out of line, and having NO limits.

Total self-control (easier said than done) is required as you attempt to obey the rules and restrictions of a diet. You'll have to control the urges, desires, and emotional eating driven by your unwanted feelings. And, if you've ever binged or cheated on a diet, you know what it is like to have a revolt brewing inside as your inner child demands to indulge in comfort foods.

You once had a very healthy appetite for life as a kid, voraciously exploring your world and eating up all the wonders that life had to offer. And it is unfortunate that your earliest lessons at self-control, a.k.a. curbing your enthusiasm, probably occurred around the same time you were being forced to contain your puppy-like, tail-wagging excitement for many things in life.

On most days, you had to sit still, pay attention, stop talking, stop playing, and hold in all of your energy to the point of bursting—or face the consequences of challenging the 'My Way or the Highway' attitude of parents, teachers, authority figures, and society at large. During that same time, you may have also noticed that most of those same adults had no zest for life—the end result of years of controlling and curbing their own appetite for enthusiasm.

Over the years, you've been taught to control what you think, say/express, do, believe, feel, hear, see, imagine, hope for—and if you are currently on a diet—what you eat.

As a child, you had to survive. So you became highly skilled at self-control, self-restraint, self-editing, self-censoring, self-judgment, self-blame, self-shame, self-sacrifice, and self-punishment—and that's just the short list.

Today, in order to cope, you've taken on the role of self-dictator—which leads to self-loathing, self-doubt, and self-sabotage. All of this is a bitter pill to swallow, especially if you use self-control to avoid letting others control you.

You would think that with so much self-control you would feel empowered and free. Yet, more than likely you chose those behaviors to keep peace with others, especially people who control your paycheck or your happiness. Individuals, who require you to jump through hoops, be at their beck and call, and do everything you SHOULD, can make you feel like you are walking on a tightrope with no room for error.

Inevitably you rebel, break the rules, and get a little out of control. That sometimes means speeding on the highway, cheating on your diet, or letting off steam with emotional outbursts.

Anything to break free from the chains of self-control that bind.

You may feel that the only thing you _are_ in control of is when you allow yourself to go out of control via socially acceptable outlets—food, addictions, or extreme sports—all of which impact your waistline, your health, and your life.

Your inner child longs to feel freedom and empowerment to do and choose what she wants. Hence, when you feel controlled, your inner child may reach for food in rebellion.

With food, you sometimes can't make any other choice but to overindulge, even if you know what is contributing to your emotional emptiness. This is especially true if you were starved of soul food (love and attention) when you were a child. You may now hoard food or gorge on it—trying to stuff it all in to stave off being physically or emotionally hungry.

This Weight Loss Discovery Journey allows you and your inner child to create an early warning system that lets you know when your emotions have been triggered <u>and</u> when your stomach has had enough—so that your soul and your stomach are emotionally and physically satisfied, satiated, and content.

By using this Weight Loss Discovery Journey to take a deeper look at your emotions and what's really eating at you, you will begin to discover healthier outlets to nourish and heal yourself. You will then be able to rekindle the zest you had for life as a child and finally <u>know that no limits</u> can truly contain that kind of enthusiasm.

<u>Your Weight Loss Discovery Journal</u>: CONTROL

For the following journal opportunities, write down what first comes to mind. And if nothing comes to mind, allow your inner child to use her imagination creatively.

1. Who or what do you feel controlled by in your life (at home, at work, in your interpersonal relationships, your finances, your health)?

EXAMPLE: I feel controlled in my life by...

2. In what areas of your life do you wish you had more freedom to be more open and express yourself?

EXAMPLE: I wish I could express myself more freely in the following areas of my life...

We interrupt this regularly scheduled reading to encourage you to return to Your Weight Loss Discovery Journal in previous chapters and invest your time in these transformation-inducing exercises.

If you have not already done so, it's to your waistline's advantage to do so now. ☺

The space in those sections has been provided to allow you to acknowledge your inner child and give her voice—so she can flex her freedom muscle and finally speak what's on her mind.

Journaling is one of the easiest and most self-empowering ways to do this, for it gives your inner child permission to Explore, Articulate, and then Transform what's really been EATing at her and weighing her down.

The journal sections are more than just a mélange of words or mere food for thought. They are words:

- For action;
- For healing; and
- For freedom from food controlling your life.

10

<u>ANGER</u>

Gnashing Your Teeth

Emotions can easily be triggered by people and events in your life; and negative feelings can rise to the surface in a flash, especially if you are already overwhelmed or stressed.

All of your emotions—positive and negative—need an outlet, like a volcano or pressure cooker that, unless it lets off a little steam, is guaranteed to blow its top.

If you cannot find healthy ways to release the weight of your negative emotions, especially your many shades of anger, then you may take it out on others in inappropriate ways. Anything to help transfer that energy out of your body, even if it's misdirected at innocents.

You probably take your unexpressed emotions out on yourself as well.

After stewing in anger for decades, you may experience a modest release of stress by gnashing your teeth on a giant piece of chocolate cake or even on your own fingernails.

This is because, as children, everyone learned to internalize the bulk of their emotional dramas and traumas. Very few people were ever allowed to fully express anger at their parents, teachers, or any authority figure. Consequently, to survive, children have to energetically control their anger, bite their tongues, and keep it all in.

And so our blood begins to boil and our anger builds up over the years for a lot of things—hurts, letdowns, disappointments, betrayals, and the injustices of life.

Most people usually control their anger out of fear—fear of letting the floodgates open. Fear that they won't be able to stop all the years of seething rage, frustration, resentment, pain, hatred, and self-hatred that's been pent up inside.

Is it any wonder you eat so much?

Your hands keep shoveling something into your mouth to keep you quiet, distracted, or to prevent you from speaking and expressing what's on your mind and what's truly in your heart.

When you are not permitted to express your anger, it remains a caged emotion, along with other unwanted feelings stuffed deep into your body. You may not even be aware of the triggers that cause your anger to surface in the first place. You just know that you are angry and that you don't really know what to do with it.

Anger can be used to mask fear and sadness. It can also be used to keep people and new experiences at a distance—as protection from any new heartbreak, pain, or disappointment. However, trying to keep hurt and anger tucked safely away only keeps you weighed down, contributing to an emotional overload as your internal pressure keeps building and building.

Plus, keeping emotions tucked away can keep weight loss goals and dreams forever out of reach. Especially if you feel angered by the fact that you <u>have</u> to lose weight and feel that being on a diet is the only answer available.

This battle leaves you forever stuck in a food dilemma with no apparent weigh out. You punish yourself whenever you eat to keep unwanted emotions in check, and then further punish yourself by dieting to shed unwanted pounds that are a direct result of controlling those unwanted emotions. You may also spend countless hours pounding the pavement or working it off/working it out at the gym; all while simultaneously striving to lose weight, de-stress, and achieve liberation from your caged emotions.

Anger, like happiness, is normal and healthy. When you complete the writing portion of each of these exercises, this Weight Loss Discovery Journey will allow you to begin to express, acknowledge, and own your anger without injury to yourself or others.

Additionally, talking to someone who is supportive and non-judgmental can be beneficial to lifting this weighted emotion from your heart and waistline.

Giving yourself permission to acknowledge that your anger exists can be the first step to seeking out a new way to successfully express it.

For the following journal opportunities, write down what first comes to mind. And if nothing comes to mind, allow your inner child to use her imagination creatively.

1. Write down what upsets you the most or makes you angry about having to lose weight.

EXAMPLE: What upsets me the most or makes me angry about having to lose weight is...

2. Write down 3 (or more) non-food related things you like to do that really light you up inside or that put a smile on your face.

EXAMPLE: The things that really light me up inside or that put a smile on my face are...

11

<u>OVERWHELMED</u>

Having A Lot On Your Plate

You're on a roll!

You are now 1/3 of the way into
Your Weight Loss Discovery Journey.

Take a moment now and pat yourself on the back! ☺

In this day and internet age, it's pretty hard not to be overwhelmed by the demands of everyday living.

We spend our days trying to stay afloat in a sea of information and data coming at us from all sides. Everything clamors for our attention: notice this, buy that, etc. To say the least, the overflow can shock your senses and your psyche.

Where does anyone find the time to absorb all this information? How are you supposed to manage your ever-elevated stress levels or keep your adrenal glands from running on overdrive?

People are also constantly vying for your time and attention at home, at work, and in all of your interpersonal relationships. Plus, technology and social media keep speeding things up, making people want things faster from you—even if it's just a response to an email, a Facebook posting, or a tweet.

People's demands on your time can often feel more unreasonable than ever before. You may be running on empty before even leaving the house. You probably feel exhausted by mid-morning and are zonked out on the couch before the evening news is over.

Our to-do lists are never-ending and always expanding as we take on more and more. Trying to keep others happy means trying to get too many things done on an already overflowing plate.

There is only so much of you to go around (unless you clone yourself). And, there are only 24 hours in a day—especially if you include sleep. The problem is, you wake up and do it all over again the next day. And the next. And the next. Like the Energizer Bunny®, you force yourself to keep going.

Juggling your to-do lists can make you feel like a Times Square traffic cop in the middle of rush hour. You continually reshuffle, reprioritize, bump things off, and add things to the list. Most of the time, you put others first and put your needs at the bottom, especially your health and well-being. And seldom do you delegate to others. Instead, you carry the weight of the world/your family/your job on your shoulders. No wonder you are swamped and weighed down by it all!

This lifestyle can get the better of anyone.

The mere thought of how much work you need to do may overwhelm and mentally stress you out to the point of being unable to function. You may very well feel like hiding under the covers and never getting out of bed.

To handle the pressures, demands, and deadlines/dreadlines that you work under, you may turn to foods you enjoy to get through your stress-filled days. Attempting to diet only creates more pressure as you prepare to banish your beloved foods— the only thing on your plate that you may like. Just the thought of it can leave you crushed and demoralized.

If that wasn't enough, following all of the rules on a diet plan can be overwhelming. When everything you like to eat is off the menu, you can hyper-focus on what you're going to eat and feed yourself. You may feel like you have to work harder to create a menu full of flavor, fun, and fuel to get you through the day.

You may resist dieting altogether because you feel that you are making enough sacrifices in other areas of your life. Plus, you already know how easily your inner child can sabotage all your dieting efforts when she's fed up as well.

You may also resist dieting because you may not want to eat differently than your spouse, significant other, family, friends, etc. You may prefer not to have the diet plate. If you eat what everyone else has, you can avoid swimming in a sea of temptation and possibly giving in and then feeling guilty later on. In any case, you may feel worn down by your conflicting thoughts about dieting on one hand and your heartfelt desire to lose weight on the other.

Luckily, this Weight Loss Discovery Journey offers you the chance to energetically shed what is weighing you down on your overflowing plate. It will help you feel like you can give yourself permission to kick your feet up, catch your breath, and finally feel more relaxed around food.

It will also allow you and your inner child to recapture your enthusiasm for food in a healthier way. After all, we all want to be like the woman in that famous restaurant movie scene and be able to say 'I'll have what's she's having' and then truly enjoy it.

For the following journal opportunities, write down what first comes to mind. And if nothing comes to mind, allow your inner child to use her imagination creatively.

1. What do you wish you could take off of your never-ending TO-DO list?

EXAMPLE: I wish I could take off the following things from my never-ending TO-DO list...

2. List 3 (or more) non-food related things in your life that you are grateful for.

EXAMPLE: The things I am grateful for in my life are...

12

<u>ATTENTION</u>

The Apple Of Someone's Eye

We all enjoy being the center of attention where all eyes and ears are focused on us. And, we all deserve to be the apple of someone's eye and have someone pay special attention to us.

For us, time is synonymous with attention. And like gold, time is a commodity in limited supply. Everyone is trying to get their slice of the time-pie from key people in their lives. And in a world full of people starving for attention and dying to be noticed, people will resort to all sorts of behaviors if they feel anything <u>you</u> are doing—even simply eating or cooking differently—could take time and attention away from <u>them</u>. Similar to love, there never seems to be enough time to go around.

Growing up, the time that people (particularly your parents) spent with you was proof that you mattered and were valued—that you were the apple of their eye.

T   Truly
I   =   I
M   Matter
E   Everyday

During that period, you learned to equate feeling loved with how much time and attention someone gave you, especially if you felt that you had to compete with others in your immediate family or could only get attention in limited amounts.

Time, love, and attention are vital nutrients for your heart. They are your soul's food. They are the core reasons you have struggled with weight loss.

If your parents spent less time with you over the years or never really paid you much attention to begin with, a part of your heart and soul may now be starving to be noticed and acknowledged.

When you feel deprived of being nourished with soul foods, you may then reach for physical food or other substances to fill up this void. That's why, when it comes to losing weight and keeping it off for good, it's beneficial to discover what's really eating at you, so that you and your inner child can begin to feel fulfilled/filled up at the deepest part of your being.

As a child, you gobbled up attention either by being good or by having a bad attitude, misbehaving, and getting in trouble. Most of us would take our attention any way we could get it. We may have even learned that our bad behavior—acted out on ourselves or on others—got us more attention than our good behavior.

We also may have unconsciously gotten sick (from a stomachache to a serious ailment) to get the attention we'd been aching for. Often we'd be treated to our favorite foods to make our aches and pains go away or just to distract us from them.

Being on a diet means paying more attention to yourself and what you are putting into your mouth. It also means depriving yourself of your beloved favorite foods, which may then remind you of your childhood deprivation of time, love, and attention. What's more, you may very well feel invisible in the body you are in now and may be willing to go on a diet and starve yourself to get thinner—all in the hopes of being noticed or to finally get the attention you deserve and have been longing for from someone in your life—your spouse, significant other, parent(s), boss, etc.

This Weight Loss Discovery Journey can help you to identify how you may be starving for attention, so that you can free your inner child from trying to fill herself up with food instead.

Looking for additional support during
<u>Your Weight Loss Discovery Journey</u>?

Then go to page 217 to learn
about the interactive program and
online community that will
empower and motivate you
on your journey.

Your Weight Loss Discovery Journal: ATTENTION

For the following journal opportunities, write down what first comes to mind. And if nothing comes to mind, allow your inner child to use her imagination creatively.

1. From whom do you wish you could get more positive/loving attention?

EXAMPLE: I wish I could get more positive/loving attention from...

2. List 3 (or more) non-food related ways that you could shower yourself with more attention.

EXAMPLE: The ways I could shower myself with more attention are...

13

<u>SUPPORT</u>

Who's Got Your Back?

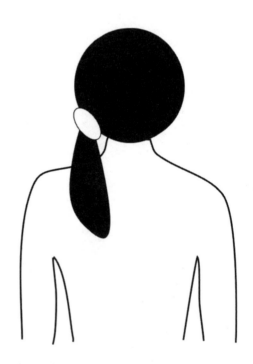

Do you feel supported by others in your life? Or are you everyone else's Rock of Gibraltar? Are you the one responsible for holding it together for everyone at home, in your extended family, in your social network, and on the job?

As women, we naturally support others and lend a helping hand, even if we are strapped for time or already overloaded. After years of watching our mothers and other women put everyone else first, we often mirror this cycle of self-sacrifice. Additionally, this gesture becomes more complicated because often we never allow ourselves to receive this same support from others.

You may feel uncomfortable asking for help, while secretly longing for someone else to provide what you need. You may also be afraid to hope that others will notice your struggle and offer their support unsolicited. And if you're lucky, you may have one or two good friends, neighbors, or co-workers who are there for you, especially in your hour of need.

Yet, if you don't feel supported—that someone's got your back—you may seek out external devices that promise to deliver this necessary extra support. These devices can come in the form of shoe inserts, firm mattresses, support hose/tights—all manufactured to provide you and your body with what you've been craving. Yet mostly, you may turn to food for solace and energy to help you get through your days and nights and to make up for how you feel neglected.

On a diet, you'll have your own demons and monsters to slay—your inner critic, self-doubt, and resistance. Diets challenge you to get serious about losing weight by demanding that you banish your favorite foods from your cupboards and fridge and to stop secretly eating/binging on foods that are not on the diet menu.

To achieve this, the diets declare that you'll have to manage your wild-and-sometimes-uncontrollable cravings, as well as your unbridled emotions. And if all else fails, you can always buy a girdle or some sort of fashionable belt to help you keep it all tucked in until the weight finally comes off.

However, you may often feel alone and isolated on a diet, jonesing for your favorite foods.

So it should be no surprise that one of the most vital keys to any weight loss success is a 24/7 support network and personal cheering squad, built from friends, family, and/or co-workers who:

- Help you as the emotions you've been stuffing down for so long start to surface;
- Offer a shoulder to cry on and tell you everything will be okay;
- Cheer you on and give you a 'You got this girl!' pep talk, especially when you are down and want to give up; and
- Pat you on your back and acknowledge you and all of your hard work with an 'Atta girl!' every once in a while.

As you build your team, be aware of saboteurs, people who claim to support you yet:

- Feel threatened by your desire to change yourself;
- Try to oppose or undermine you, instead of dealing with their own issues; and
- Try to get you to cheat on your diet by tempting you with foods.

You'll also need to get your inner child fully on board and let her have a say in the matter. After all, she's got just as much wisdom as you do when it comes to your body. You just may not have been listening to her wants and needs.

When you receive the support you need through time, love, and attention, you will then feel more capable of achieving your weight loss goals.

A support system can act as a sounding board and can serve you just the right amount of recognition and encouragement, ending the need to use food as a substitute to fill up your heart and soul.

Your 24/7 support network will help you stay the course.

And having a 24/7 support network firmly in place will also help to keep the pounds off for good after you reach your weight loss goals.

Your Weight Loss Discovery Journey will allow you to begin to feel safe and comfortable enough to ask others in your life for their support or seek out new forms of support.

<u>Your Weight Loss Discovery Journal</u>: SUPPORT

For the following journal opportunities, write down what first comes to mind. And if nothing comes to mind, allow your inner child to use her imagination creatively.

1. How and by whom do you feel neglected or unsupported at this moment in your life?

EXAMPLE: I feel neglected and unsupported at this moment in my life in the following ways by the following people...

2. Write down the strongest parts of your body and briefly describe how those areas help you live your life and thrive in your body.

EXAMPLE: I feel that the following parts of my body are the strongest and that they help me to...

14

ACCEPTANCE

Seal Of Approval

In our heart of hearts, we all want to be truly loved and accepted for who we are—quirks and all. Unfortunately, we often only receive love when we act as a mirror or extension of others. Because of our fear of rejection, strong survival instincts, and desire for approval—a lot of 'Mini-Me' type behaviors will manifest from choosing a similar career path, clothing, attitude, or even marrying a particular spouse. If approval is still not forthcoming, we may become what someone else wants us to be, instead of who we are truly meant to be.

When people in your life, especially your parents, do not fully accept you or blatantly reject you, it pierces the very core of your being. You may then find it hard to accept yourself or your body. This may include your quirks and personality traits, as well as your intellect, creativity, dreams, aspirations, and emotions. These all get pushed away if you've been told that they are unwanted, unreasonable, and unrealistic.

This, in turn, hurts your inner child who will resort to approval-seeking behaviors, or worse, will shut down and hide those parts of herself that have been rejected. She may even begin to unknowingly give birth to a slew of detrimental body image issues. This of course leads to poor self-esteem.

As your body blossomed during puberty, you may have felt embarrassed and wanted to hide. You also may have accentuated, enhanced, or flaunted parts of your body that garnered attention. Since we all learn to equate attention with love, this left many of us looking for love in all the wrong places.

You may want to change certain parts of your body that you consider flawed. You may want them to be smaller, bigger, taller, longer, shorter, lighter, darker, curlier, straighter, firmer, softer—the list is endless and can vary with your moods and emotions, as well as with your age.

In your quest to achieve the perfect body/perfect woman/perfect version of you that will finally get you the love, acceptance, and attention you've been longing for, you may go against your own inner truth.

This can become an endless cycle of trying to prove your worthiness—one in which you keep begging for acceptance into the group or tribe you wish to join. Their seal of approval is like gold for it displays your worth to others. It starts in your family, continues in your peer groups in high school and college, and then straight on into adulthood.

When someone accepts us, we feel confident that anything is possible for us to be, do, or have. Yet, until we learn to believe in ourselves, our abilities, and our worth, we may choose to compromise who we are in order to get the sustenance of being accepted as part of a group.

Being on a diet is mostly about wanting the physical parts of your body to be smaller or in better shape than they are at present. Giving up things you like to eat while on a diet may just serve to remind you of all the ways you have sacrificed to fit in, belong, and gain the approval and acceptance of others.

Now that you are firmly on you Your Weight Loss Discovery Journey, give yourself a moment to reflect on what parts of your body/being you have a hard time accepting, so you can begin to accept them in a good way. For when you do so, you then give yourself permission to let yourself and your inner child back into your own heart and soul. This will then allow you to shower yourself with the nurturing waterfall of self-acceptance—which can help to bring you peace and relaxation.

Allow yourself to return home to who you were meant to be and in the body you were always meant to be in.

For the following journal opportunities, write down what first comes to mind. And if nothing comes to mind, allow your inner child to use her imagination creatively.

1. What parts of your body/your being do you have a hard time accepting?

EXAMPLE: It's difficult for me to accept the following parts of my body/my being...

2. What parts of your body/your being do you like and accept?

EXAMPLE: I like and accept the following parts of my body/my being...

15

<u>FAMILY</u>

It's All Relative

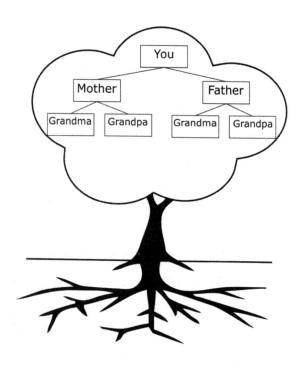

Food = Love

Food is a form of love and love is the foundation of family life. Our mothers nourished themselves so that they could sustain us. In their wombs, we had everything we needed from food to precise temperature control to feeling supported and protected. Our mothers even bore our weight until the time of our birth.

In this new outer world, our food supply and eating habits shifted slightly as we were nursed with our mother's milk—otherwise known as 'liquid love'. And if our mothers had no milk or didn't want to breastfeed us, then we were given formula instead.

It was a precious time for most of us, as we had to be held closely by anyone trying to feed us—cradled to support and protect our fragile little bodies. Plus, our cries usually got us an immediate response, and we were showered with time and attention (the soul's foods) and given what we may have needed in the moment to soothe those cries—food, loving contact, or a diaper change.

Our feed-me-when-I'm-hungry on-demand crying system served us well for a few short years. Then, as we moved from liquid-based to more solid-based foods, we learned to wait until those in control of our food supply were ready to feed us at regularly scheduled mealtimes.

We also learned that others would reward us with food for complying with their wishes. They also would use food to punish us with or without a reason—forcing us to eat, not giving us enough, or making us go totally without it. At which point, our relationship with food started to become complicated with all the mixed messages we received—leaving us a little bewildered.

Food = Reward or Punishment = Confusion.

A lot happened around food within our families. Mealtimes may have been relaxed, fun, and a time when you were acknowledged, given attention, and allowed to share what went on during your day. All of this filled up your heart and soul—and your stomach. You may have many fond memories related to food from birthday parties, snack times, holidays, barbeques, picnics, etc.

Or you may not.

Instead, you may have eaten in total silence, total chaos or total tension/stress, and under total control of one or both of your parents. You may have been trained with table manners ranging from how to sit/eat properly all the way to knowing when it was your turn to speak (if you even got the chance to). You may have eaten totally alone—at the table, in front of the TV or computer, or in your room—if others were too busy to sit down with you or were just not around. If you came from a large family or there was never enough food, you may have learned to be quick and gobble up what you could. Additionally, mealtimes may have felt more like an interrogation and you may have opted to keep food stuffed in your mouth to avoid responding.

At the table, there may have been a lot of tension and emotionally charged conversations between your parents, and they may have been the only two allowed to speak (or argue). You may have been in fear of your safety, especially if the situation escalated beyond mere words.

In addition to everything else going on in your house, you also learned to deal or not deal with your emotions, based on the example of your parents and others in your family. You may have quickly learned to express only the acceptable emotions, especially if you wanted to avoid punishment. At this point, you may have innocently begun to reach for food to stuff down any unwanted emotions—unwittingly turning yourself into an emotional eater.

You picked up many food habits from your family that may still be with you today—how you eat, what you eat, when you eat, and why you eat. All of these habits have an emotional component which can drive you to eat when triggered.

Your family may or may not have shown you how to cook, so you would be able to nourish yourself. You may even have been forbidden to be in the kitchen outside of mealtimes. Conversely, you may have been forced to fend for yourself if others were busy, not around, or believed that making you more independent would serve you later on in life. More than likely, it made you feel alone or isolated.

You also have participated in other events that involved food with extended family, schoolmates, friends, co-workers, and surrogate families. Whether you had positive or negative experiences at those events, you bring them all with you every time you gather with people to share food and drink.

Additionally, you may hide what you eat or only eat certain foods when you are alone.

It's pretty safe to say that a lot of your deepest hurts and disappointments—what you didn't get or get enough of—have their roots in your family of origin. This reality can make any family gathering stressful and anxiety-filled. Everyone plays their familiar roles and knows exactly which button to press to get you to react in your habitual ways—even if you no longer live under the same roof. Plus, your current belief system, values, insights, and inspirations—even how you now feed and nourish yourself—may differ from your family and be the cause of disagreements.

Your family may not give you the freedom to be who you are or who you want to be. Instead, they may remind you of all the sacrifices they made on your behalf and your duty to fulfill their expectations.

In most parents' minds, you are still a child; and to get you to comply with their wishes, they may refer to you in either the second person (you), by your formal name, or talk as if you aren't even there. They may also try to guilt you or humiliate you to get you to do their bidding—leaving you feeling frustrated and permanently stuck.

This lack of freedom can then make you feel weighed down. It can also totally eat you up inside, and you may find yourself overeating and overdrinking to keep your mouth and hands full and keep your emotions from rising to the surface at any sort of family gathering or reunion.

In addition, if you are married, have a family, or are a caregiver, you may find it next to impossible to be on a diet because others may be very demanding of your time and expect you to cook for them in a certain way. They may also act out or try to sabotage your dieting efforts if they perceive your efforts as negatively impacting them. You may not have the time and energy to cook for yourself, let alone eat differently than everyone else. Either way, you may be left stewing in anger or resentment at always having to serve others first while your waistline expands on the sidelines.

Your inner child could benefit from expressing what she holds in and carries around with her. When you give yourself permission to look at things that bring you both joy and turmoil, you will acknowledge the internal division in your heart and can begin to heal it. You will then experience more freedom to be who you truly are in relationship to other people—which in turn allows you to connect and relate to them in new ways—even if it's the same old cast of characters.

Your Weight Loss Discovery Journey has been designed to bring you back to moments of clarity, so that you can begin to safely and easily move away from food as reward or punishment. Instead, you will reconnect with food in a more loving way that nourishes your body in the outer world and your heart and soul in your inner world.

Your Weight Loss Discovery Journal: FAMILY

For the following journal opportunities, write down what first comes to mind. And if nothing comes to mind, allow your inner child to use her imagination creatively.

1. Who or what about your family (of origin and/or present) frustrates you, makes you mad, or disappoints you?

EXAMPLE: The following people or things related to my family frustrate me, make me mad, or disappoint me...

2. List 3 (or more) non-food activities that you enjoy sharing/doing with your family.

EXAMPLE: The activities that I enjoy sharing/doing with my family are...

16

<u>BOUNDARIES</u>

Cut-Off Point

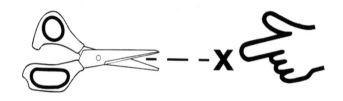

Our parents were responsible for setting boundaries for us when we were small children—partially for our safety and partially to control us so as to make their lives and the lives of other adults easier. However, if not reflected upon, those boundaries can inflict countless restrictions, confines, restraints, and limitations on our daily lives.

Our parents and those in authority let us know the lay of the land with their 'My Way or the Highway' requirements. And when they insisted that we color inside the lines, what they often meant was that we were to <u>live our lives inside all of the lines</u>.

As kids, we tested the limits of those boundaries a lot trying to gauge just how far we could really go. And when we went beyond the outer limits or simply stepped out of bounds, we suffered the consequences, which seemed to grow in severity with any repeated offense.

Your parents may have set all sorts of boundaries, limits, and conditions for you when they were structuring your life and your schedule. This probably included imposing rules on bedtimes, chores, curfews, TV time, phone time, computer time, friends, food, physical possessions, activities, and homework.

The boundaries set for you may have been very rigid and strictly enforced. Yet if you were lucky, your parents may have been more lenient about setting boundaries for you and may have even invited you to participate in setting them.

In addition to boundaries and conditions created for your physical well-being, other energetic boundaries may have been set as well. These boundaries relate to the emotional, mental, and spiritual realms.

What may have been the norm for you and your family may not have been normal for another, and you wouldn't know there was a difference until you compared your family life with someone else's.

You may have had a family structure where boundaries were complicated and/or unhealthy or inappropriate on a variety of levels. This may have left you feeling unsure where others ended and you began.

Living in a world without a physical or energetic line of demarcation may have caused you to spend your days in total confusion. And that could have left you caught between trying to please others to get the nourishment of time, love, and attention you deserved to living in fear for your life and your safety.

You may have never known what defines a healthy or appropriate boundary. And you still might not know that today.

Self-exploration and healing work allows you to discover and implement healthy boundaries with people in your family and in the workplace, as well as with your friends and in your romantic relationships.

You get to consciously choose what are acceptable and welcome forms of behavior from others. You also get to choose what behaviors are unacceptable and unwelcome.

You have a right to say when anyone else's behavior makes you uncomfortable <u>and</u> ask them to stop. You can even remove yourself from their company momentarily or permanently.

When we are young and the adults in our lives have inappropriate boundaries with us, we unconsciously carry that inappropriateness into all of our interpersonal relationships. It may feel impossible to even create healthy boundaries—and even more impossible to keep those boundaries in place with others and with ourselves, especially as they relate to food.

Sometimes carrying extra weight on your body is the only energetic form of a boundary you can create for yourself—a body-as-a-buffer-zone to physically keep people away from you. The extra weight may also serve as padding necessary to help you brace yourself from the impact from the blows that life may deal you—physically, mentally, or emotionally—real or imagined.

The extra weight may allow you to unconsciously send messages to others, such as:

- Don't come near me
- Don't hug me
- Don't touch me
- Don't look at me that way
- Don't say those sorts of things to me
- Don't hurt me
- Don't harm me, etc.

Any or all of the above may help your inner child to create a physical barrier around your body to protect your heart and your emotional heart (a.k.a. your stomach) from experiencing any kind of pain or disappointment.

And what you truly think of thin people or a thinner version of yourself absolutely brings all of these issues to the surface.

You may have already discovered a few things about yourself when you did Your Weight Loss Discovery Journal exercises at the end of the 'Thin People' chapter. And what you discovered there may indicate why the extra weight is currently on your body—for protection, for safety, for strength.

Food may help you keep your body-as-a-buffer-zone padding. Or it may keep unwanted emotions at bay—emotions that surface in all your interpersonal relationships, especially if you have no boundaries with others or have a hard time keeping your own personal boundaries in place.

A diet means not going beyond the boundaries set by that diet. And as already mentioned in the 'Control' chapter, you may consciously choose to have no limits with food from time to time because you feel excessively controlled/limited/bound in all other areas of your life; forcing some part of you to rebel and go outside the lines.

Your Weight Loss Discovery Journey provides you with a specific set of exercises within each chapter to help you safely find clarity about underlying issues physically weighing down your body.

Clarity will allow you to easily give yourself permission to stop worrying about what everyone else wants, so you can focus on what you want to accomplish and how you want to be treated. Clarity gently brings to the surface reserves of strength within the frontier of your heart. Clarity allows you to be peacefully present with yourself every time you are around food. Clarity helps you discover what you want your life to look like, and then allows your being to live in it, unbounded, every day.

Your Weight Loss Discovery Journal: BOUNDARIES

For the following journal opportunities, write down what first comes to mind. And if nothing comes to mind, allow your inner child to use her imagination creatively.

1. Who do you wish you could limit contact with or only see every once in awhile in your life?

EXAMPLE: I wish I could limit contact with the following people in my life ...

2. Write down 3 (or more) non-food related activities or things that make you feel completely free.

EXAMPLE: The activities or things that make me feel completely free are...

17
<u>HOPELESS</u>
Pit Of Despair

There may be times when you will despair of ever achieving your weight loss goals. With neither an internal nor external pep squad to keep you going, you may very well feel like you've reached the end of your ability to persevere—which can lead you to choose to curl up with a chocolate cake, a habitual solution for feelings of defeat and failure.

If you suffer from a complete loss of faith in yourself and in your abilities to get what you want, the slightest push can tumble you into the pit of despair, where the light that shines on your goal dims to a fading glimmer in the distance. And once you've landed in the pit, you may feel that any further effort on your part would be pointless, especially if you are a few weeks into your diet and seeing slow results, no results, or results that have already plateaued. That terrible hopeless feeling makes your heart ache.

And that is exactly the time when 'Why Bother' rears its head.

Like a weed that just keeps regenerating no matter how hard or how often you pull it up at the roots, 'Why Bother' brings with it resistance that is bent on sabotaging your efforts. It achieves this by getting you to throw in the towel on your weight loss journey.

And resistance can be relentless.

While this internal battle rages on, there may be people in your life—family, friends, or others—who add turmoil to any remaining glimmer of hope you have of achieving your goals. They do this by telling you not to set your expectations too high. These people may try to discourage you because some part of them fears your success will change the relationship they have with you. They may be at a point where they have nothing to look forward to in life or may have given up on themselves and their dreams a long time ago—and it is safer and more comfortable for them to encourage you to do the same. These people see you in a way that is comfortable for them. And, they may be threatened by who you could potentially become.

If you are still trying to prove your worth to others, your own inner child may unconsciously sabotage your efforts in order to prove them right. This abandonment of yourself leaves your inner child feeling like there is no way out of the pit of despair and no way to win the acceptance and acknowledgment that she craves. She may then reach for food to fill up the empty space she feels in her heart while simultaneously trying to numb the ache.

Moreover, you also feel compelled to fulfill the expectations of experts—parents, teachers, bosses, health professionals—because it makes you anxious to consider that they may be wrong.

Remember that you are in charge—and that everybody is different—so if you don't like an opinion, seek out another until you find one or several that are in alignment with your goals and that offer you continued hope and support.

Carrying around your own resistance coupled with dealing with discouraging people is exhausting. It can make you feel abandoned and without the support you want and need to reach your weight loss goals.

Fortunately, your Weight Loss Discovery Journey can help you let go of the weight of living someone else's version of your reality. It will also help you to let the light that is always shining within the heart of your inner child illuminate a path out of the pit of despair. For it reminds you that there is an abundance of things to look forward to in life.

Your Weight Loss Discovery Journal: HOPELESS

For the following journal opportunities, write down what first comes to mind. And if nothing comes to mind, allow your inner child to use her imagination creatively.

1. What have others told you not to get your hopes up about in life, especially when it comes to dieting/losing weight?

EXAMPLE: People have told me not to get my hopes up about the following things...

2. What do you look forward to happening in your life when you lose weight?

EXAMPLE: I look forward to the following things happening in my life when I lose weight...

18

DEPRESSED

Dark Cloud Hanging Over You

All of your emotions and feelings reside inside your body, mind, and heart. And they all need an outlet.

When you have unexpressed emotions, they begin to build up and weigh you down. The resulting energetic heaviness can then drain you of the strength necessary to get out of bed in the morning, let alone make it through the day.

Your heart becomes heavy way before your physical body does.

And for this reason, the weightiness that your heart currently feels probably saddens and discourages you—maybe the way it did when you were a little girl. You may have intense feelings of hopelessness, a bottomless pit of despair, that is next to impossible to escape. Everything feels pointless, your hopes and dreams seem like a cruel joke, and you can't imagine things ever changing for the better. You may even wish it would all just come to an end, so you could stop feeling so empty inside.

If you are or have been depressed, you know that no words could truly express your immense feelings of sadness. Everyone on the planet has experienced these dark nights of the soul, yet not everyone admits to it. However, if these feelings continue for more than two weeks, you may need additional help to balance your brain chemistry. Seeking outside professional support for your body and mind can be an asset to the self-help work you are doing here.

In a depressed mind space, all of your 'why bother doing anything' thoughts and dark emotions seem heightened, yet ironically cause you to hit new lows. If you could only get the scale to go as low as you feel inside, then it might start to clear the dark clouds. In this state, each time you hypnotically reach for food, you may simply be crying for help.

114

And since food provides a release of nutrients and chemicals into your body, triggering emotional memories of love, comfort, and relief, it can be used to quell or quench your unexpressed emotions.

Unchecked, we can use food to comfort, soothe, or numb ourselves when our pain is too much to bear or if our efforts seem doomed to failure.

Following the rules of a diet plan can be depressing in and of itself, especially when you think of the possible time commitment involved. You may be excited to become a slimmer version of yourself, yet nothing may inspire or motivate you on your diet, especially if your weight loss goal seems unreachable.

And depending on what you eat on that diet, all of your moods and emotions may be impacted, potentially swinging all over the place. You may experience a 'down in the dumps' side to a 'don't piss me off, agitated, angry' side. Even if you eat healthier than ever before, you may still be grumpy because your beloved comfort foods are on a forbidden list. And you may be grumpier still if you feel like you are being forced to do something that you don't really want to do.

Courageously looking at what you find depressing about trying to lose weight will help you to win the weight loss battle in your mind. When you do that, winning on the scale becomes nearly effortless.

Rather than simply trying to depress your appetite by going on a diet, give your inner child the chance to find alternative ways to feel filled up with physical food and other soul foods, while keeping the pounds off for good.

For the following journal opportunities, write down what first comes to mind. And if nothing comes to mind, allow your inner child to use her imagination creatively.

1. What depresses you the most about dieting?

EXAMPLE: What depresses me the most about dieting is...

2. List 3 (or more) people, pets/animals, places, or activities that cheer you up or make you feel happy.

EXAMPLE: The people, pets/animals, places, or activities that cheer me up or make me feel happy are...

If you've been eagerly reading through the chapters and bypassing the writing exercises, it's to your benefit to go back to any previous chapter and take a moment to write in Your Weight Loss Discovery Journal.

Reading alone is great and can provide you with new ideas, yet doing the exercises helps you to accelerate your results by tuning in to your inner child and giving her a voice. This ensures that you both are in alignment with your goal of losing weight and toning up your adult body.

19

FRUSTRATED

Have Had It Up To Here

100

0

The moment of truth on any diet comes when you step on a scale to judge your weight loss progress.

You may follow a specific weigh-in routine like some sort of Olympic athlete. You may weigh yourself when you first get up, or only after you go to the bathroom, or only with clothes on, or only in the buff, or only at the gym or only before you go to sleep.

You know your routine.

You are always hoping for positive progress. Anything to prove to yourself that all of your efforts are not in vain and that something is working: shopping for foods on the diet, cooking in a healthy way, putting your beloved favorite foods on an extended time-out, avoiding temptation, steering clear of social gatherings, sacrificing sleep and downtime to exercise, and replacing crunching food in your mouth with crunches at the gym for your stomach. Unfortunately, the number glaring back at you from the face of the scale isn't always a happy smiley one.

If you don't like what you first see, you may get off and on the scale several times. You might even try to convince yourself that the scale is off, or at the very least, needs new batteries—that is unless you are weighing yourself on the gold standard of scales like the one at the doctor's office.

If your weight hasn't changed or you've gained back a pound or two, you may wonder if it's water weight or muscle weight, as muscle weighs more than fat. Or, you might be getting close to your time of the month and you know how unpredictable that can be.

At last, you step off the scale totally discouraged and frustrated. You curse the scale and then may resort to other tactics to confirm to yourself you are losing weight such as measuring yourself if you didn't like what the scale had to show you. Your last resort may be to try on clothes—especially your skinny jeans. You tell yourself you'll be happy when something that hasn't fit you for a long time finally does.

You now try to pick out what you are going to wear for the day. This may be an ordeal as you resent having to put on larger-sized clothing. Instead, you may attempt to stuff your body into something that just barely fits you or doesn't really hang right. Whatever the case may be, it may take you forever to put something on and feel comfortable enough to walk out of your room and then out your front door.

It's a total shock to your system and your motivation first thing in the morning to have those sorts of disappointments. You may choose to not eat breakfast, yet that's okay since you are running late and don't really have the time to prepare anything on the diet menu. Plus, you try to fool yourself into believing you could go without the extra calories and still have the energy you need to make it through your long day.

You set about chastising yourself about how you'll have to just try harder. Yet, a part of you has had it up to here and then some with dieting. You want to lose weight so badly that you try everything. And still you can't lose the weight or get the scale to smile up at you when you step on it.

You feel like the only way to lose weight is to be on a diet and give up all the foods you like to eat; yet once on a diet, you always end up feeling restricted, trying to contain an energy about to explode. You also feel resentful and punished. Resentful of all the other people, including some of your women friends and even family members, who seem to be able to eat whatever they want and don't have a weight issue. Punished at always trying to avoid temptation on a diet and feeling guilty if you give in to that temptation. And maybe even frustrated at having to cook for others in your family who insist that you serve the foods they want, instead of eating the foods that are best for you.

Up until now, you may have experienced many frustrated attempts at losing weight. And every morning when you go to weigh yourself or get dressed, you have to deal with the same 'Why Bother' thoughts over and over again.

Giving up would make things so much easier in the short run. Yet you now know that so many other things—unfulfilled needs, unexpressed emotions, unresolved issues—are linked to how weighed down you feel. And you now know how all this makes you feel when you step on the scale to physically weigh yourself.

Your Weight Loss Discovery Journey will continue to help you recognize all the things that are frustrating you, so that you will naturally begin to allow yourself to step back from all the other ways you define yourself. This, in turn, will encourage you to seek out new ways to weigh and measure all of your successes—ways that are sure to bring a smile to your face.

Your Weight Loss Discovery Journal: FRUSTRATED

For the following journal opportunities, write down what first comes to mind. And if nothing comes to mind, allow your inner child to use her imagination creatively.

1. Briefly describe how you feel when you don't get the weight loss results you want.

(For a sample list of negative feelings, go to the Appendix on page 215. Or, go to:
http://gtthotp.com/handouts/gtthotp%20negative.pdf)

EXAMPLE: When I don't get the results I want, I feel...

2. Write down 3 (or more) of your non-food related successes.

EXAMPLE: The successes that I have had recently that don't involve food are...

20

<u>STUCK</u>

Spinning Your Wheels

You know that every time you've lost weight, you start to feel happy and rejoice in your good fortune. You also then expect the weight to continue to come off at its current pace. Yet, that may not always be the case.

Instead, you may encounter a weight loss plateau where you can go no lower. Or worse, you may start regaining the pounds. In either case, you may feel stuck, reminded of all of the other times in your life where you have felt:

- Stuck at the table being forced to eat foods you hated;
- Stuck doing schoolwork and other things you didn't want to do;
- Stuck with doing it the way your parents and others wanted it done;
- Stuck with no real outlet for your unwanted emotions; and
- Stuck seeking solace in food for your unfulfilled cravings for love and attention.

Like the previous times you've been stuck, your efforts may seem like they're going nowhere and that you're wasting your precious time. You may be trying as hard as you can and may not be achieving much. It may feel like you'll never be able to overcome your habits and patterns, let alone figure out what you are doing wrong so that you can get across the weight loss finish line.

When you feel stuck on your diet, some part of you is unable—or unwilling—to move forward. If you start to regain weight, you may endlessly replay every meal you've eaten over the last several days/weeks. And if you haven't curled up with any of the beloved foods that you may still be fixated on, you might think you are being punished for something you didn't do. You may choose to cut back on the amount of food you are now eating.

Or, you may also choose to exercise more...or add exercising into the weight loss mix/recipe if you hadn't already done so.

In addition to feeling stuck on a diet, there may be other areas of your life where you feel varying levels of stuck-ness as well. You may feel stuck by an overwhelming workload, yet find yourself unable to start or stay focused on anything.

You may also feel stuck at your job or trapped in all of your interpersonal relationships by all sorts of legal and financial obligations leaving you with no way out. Plus, key people in your life may be trying to consciously or unconsciously prevent you from achieving any of your goals—including your weight loss goals.

As your mind goes around in circles trying to find a way to un-stick you, remember this: just because you haven't been able to find a solution in the past doesn't mean a solution doesn't exist. Try to sustain that glimmer of hope for your future, and remind yourself that even if you're not where you want to be in life today, you still deserve to succeed.

Allow your inner child to gently unglue her feet from the ground, easily shake off what is weighing her down, and swiftly remove the energetic obstacles blocking the path to your goals.

Every single chapter on Your Weight Loss Discovery Journey is designed to help both of you do just that—get your engines revved up, so that you can go from stuck to unstoppable.

For the following journal opportunities, write down what first comes to mind. And if nothing comes to mind, allow your inner child to use her imagination creatively.

1. What or who do you feel stuck with in life (at home, at work, in your relationships)?

EXAMPLE: I feel stuck with the following people or things/responsibilities in my life...

2. Write down 3 (or more) short phrases or words that remind you that you are unstoppable.

EXAMPLE: The short phrases or words that remind me that I'm unstoppable are...

21

<u>SWEETNESS</u>

Filling Up Your Soul's Sweet Tooth

Woo hoo! You made it through
the chapter on being Stuck.

So glad that you and your inner child were able to unglue your
feet and keep things moving right along. And what a
perfect spot to land—right into Sweetness.

Life can be unkind and bitter, especially with all the pain and disappointment that comes our way. As a direct result, we may find ourselves craving sugar in its many splendid forms—sweetness to put in our mouths. If we feel that life has been tough to swallow or has left us with a bad or unappealing taste in our mouths, we may opt to fill up with our favorite sweets:

- Candy
- Cookies
- Cakes
- Desserts
- Chocolate-anything
- Ice cream
- Pastries
- Cereals
- Protein bars (candy bars in disguise)
- Fruits
- Fruit juices
- Alcohol
- Sodas
- Flavored waters

Even children's medicine is disguised with sweeteners.

Now as an adult, you may want to be surrounded by sugary sweetness all the time; yet on an energetic level you are probably craving something else.

Sweets and sweetness are associated with more than just sugar, candy, foods, and drinks. They are also linked with non-food things such as:

- Home
- Love
- Success
- Flowers
- Music
- Harmony
- Emotions/feelings
- Goodness
- Satisfaction
- Gratification
- Wholesomeness
- Freshness
- Pureness
- Gentleness
- Kindness
- Thoughtfulness
- Pleasantness
- Delightfulness
- Attractiveness
- Friendliness
- Personality
- Humor
- Appeal
- Skill-level

If you've got a bona fide, food related sweet tooth that needs filling up on a regular basis at the sweetness refueling station, you may very well be longing for others to be sweet to you, or to show/give you kindness. You may also be craving for someone to be interested in you romantically. Or to love you—especially your parents.

Anything that is sweet to your senses or to your mind helps to satisfy your heart and soul's sweet tooth. Plus, one act or touch of kindness—by others, or even by you to yourself—could start to bring down the whole walled and protective fortress you may have built up around your heart.

We all want to enjoy all the sweetness life has to offer us. Yet, if we can't get enough of the non-food forms of sweetness (love, kindness, etc.) to help our inner child fill her heart and soul, then we may reach for a sweetness substitute in the form of food, drink, drugs, and other addictive substances.

We often associate sweetness with birthdays and other celebrations, many of which involved difficult family members, so we unconsciously sweetened them up by eating all the sugary desserts and dishes we could get our hands on. You may now reach for sweets when the bittersweet, sorrow-filled, or resentment-filled memories of your past surface, or when you have to attend a family gathering. After all, it was supposed to be a 'Home Sweet Home' versus the reality of a home that was unpleasant, endured, or survived.

We also sweeten our words to others, so that we can get what we want or have our own way. Or we sugarcoat them, to take the sting out as we deliver a tough message.

Nature, too, plays a role in the sweetness factor. Foods that are sweet to the tongue help us to identify sources of energy-rich nourishment; whereas foods that are bitter can serve to warn and help identify potential toxins and poisons.

Similarly, love and kindness (non-food forms of sweetness) are energy-rich nourishment for our souls; bitterness, a form of toxin and poison. Hence, it's to our benefit to learn to rely on our souls to help us steer clear of the latter and the people who spew those acrid substances.

Use this chapter as an opportunity to discover what other non-food forms of sweetness you are craving, so you can begin to fill up your heart and soul's sweet tooth with those instead.

Your Weight Loss Discovery Journal: SWEETNESS

For the following journal opportunities, write down what first comes to mind. And if nothing comes to mind, allow your inner child to use her imagination creatively.

1. Who do you wish would be more kind and gentle with you in your life?

EXAMPLE: I wish the following people in my life would be more kind and gentle to me...

2. Write down 3 (or more) non-food related things that you find pleasing to your senses (sight, hearing, smell, touch, and taste).

EXAMPLE: I find the following things pleasing to my senses...

22

EASINESS

Piece Of Cake

We all want life as an adult to be easy; yet let's face it, it's no piece of cake. It's challenging and difficult on some days and stressful and downright depressing on others—which sounds an awful lot like being on a diet.

When life feels hard to you or you feel burdened with everyday and mundane tasks, you may procrastinate, especially if your heart is not in it.

You obviously make it less easy on yourself when you procrastinate. Not doing what you know needs to be done and waiting until the last possible moment or not doing it at all forces you to suffer the consequences of this weighty behavior. Just think of all of the school assignments, work projects, proposals, and speeches that you left hanging until the final hour, not to mention waiting to pay your taxes until April 14th at midnight.

In addition to tasks that are difficult for you to complete, you may feel stuck in relationships with people at home, at work, or in your social network that are hard on you. Even as you hope that these relationships will get easier, you may find it difficult to extricate yourself from them.

Reaching for your favorite foods feels like the only solution to surviving tough people on tough days. This makes it even harder to stay on a diet, since giving up your beloved favorite foods just adds to the harshness of the ordeal.

On top of that, you may find it hard to fit exercising, shopping for diet foods, and cooking into your packed schedule when you already feel emotionally drained. The diet, and everything else in your life, may feel too controlled with no room for any sort of joy. On a diet, you are stuck once again trying hard to control your habits and food cravings.

You may even have conflicting thoughts related to the words easy and hard. You may worry that others may think you are lazy or not a hard-worker if you can easily/effortlessly get something done. Your parents and others may have mirrored to you that only hard-won tasks and achievements are worth your time. Because of this, you may have taken on many unpleasant and arduous tasks over the years to prove your similar work ethic.

You could find yourself stuck in a dilemma because you may believe that you need to work really hard and put in a lot of effort—literally laboring for weeks, days, and years—to lose weight. Hence, you may have unknowingly struggled through a multitude of diet attempts that your heart truly wasn't in—then or now.

Go easy and be patient with yourself if you discover that this is part of your mindset, for you and your inner child unconsciously took on those rigid beliefs and behaviors in your quest to be acknowledged and validated by parents and others.

You and your inner child have truly been working hard your whole life just to win/get/fill up with all the soul food (love, attention, etc.) you've been starving for. And since soul food has not always been forthcoming, it seems easier for you to reach for food and try to fill up on that instead.

Yet another way to fill up and calm down when life is less joy-filled is by easing into more non-food related events that you actually enjoy doing.

Physical, mental, emotional, or spiritual activities that make your heart sing, your soul laugh, and your feet dance spark memories of true childhood joy.

You may enjoy doing any number of things from the following list:

- Spending time with a friend/friends or supportive family members
- Listening to music
- Dancing and moving your body
- Doing a hobby
- Creating anything with your hands (painting, drawing, photography, etc.)
- Getting a massage
- Meditating/praying
- Sleeping in
- Taking a bath
- Swimming in the ocean
- Sitting on the beach and watching the ocean
- Reading a good/inspirational book
- Seeing a heartfelt/inspirational movie
- Listening to/watching inspirational talk show/radio show
- Going for a walk/hike
- Spending time out in nature
- Playing games/sports with others with no score/no winner
- Comedy and things that make your belly laugh
- Yoga/tai chi/qi gong
- And the list goes on ☺

Because the activities listed above help to fill up your heart and soul, doing more of them can actually help you to more readily and easily dig into the other tasks on your to-do list that you still need to accomplish.

You want life to be relaxed and nourishing, and you want taking care of yourself to be simple and easy. Additionally, you and your inner child deserve to have it your way, especially when you are both fed up with following everybody else's rules.

When you make use of all that you are learning about yourself on Your Weight Loss Discovery Journey, including joyful memories, life eases up. And when your life takes on this level of ease, grace comes into your life. There is less struggle and things just come to you, often without you trying to control anything.

You may even notice that you have a different level of open-mindedness and a willingness to explore and try new things. Even the simple act of acknowledging who is tough on you and what is difficult to take or unpleasant to do, begins to energetically free you up from how this may have been weighing you down.

An immediate benefit to this newfound lightness is that it can then help you to easily find solutions to all that you find hard to do.

You are ready to make your life a whole lot easier, aren't you?

Your Weight Loss Discovery Journal: EASINESS

For the following journal opportunities, write down what first comes to mind. And if nothing comes to mind, allow your inner child to use her imagination creatively.

1. Who is hard on you? And what is hard for you to take and do?

EXAMPLE: The following person is/people are hard on me...

EXAMPLE: And the following things are hard for me to take and do...

2. List 3 (or more) non-food related things that are easy for you to do.

EXAMPLE: The things that are easy for me to do are...

23

<u>FULLNESS</u>

Fueling The Soul

On our overflowing planet, every physical want and need can now be fulfilled, especially since items that were luxuries a few decades ago are now available to many. Plus, everyday inventions and advances in technology are designed to keep making life easier.

Because of this, you can surround yourself with physical possessions and gadgets galore—stuffing your house, closet, and cupboard to the brink. Likewise, you may fill up your physical body with food and drink until you burst at the seams. Yet even so, a part of you can still feel empty inside.

Your heart and soul long to be filled up with love and attention—the soul's food—in order to keep you going and keep parts of you alive that may feel bare, hidden, or closed off. Especially your heart.

To fill up the empty spaces inside, you may now overeat and stuff yourself to the point of feeling sick. Unlike a gas gauge in a car that alerts you when the tank is filled, your stomach doesn't have a reliable inner gauge to tell you and your inner child when you've had enough and need to stop.

Many factors can contribute to this.

Maybe you learned to eat past the point of fullness as a kid because you never knew where your next meal would come from. Or, maybe you were made to clean your plate, shamed that you were not thinking of other starving children. Or, maybe you were made to feel ungrateful if you didn't eat everything in sight, since your caregiver slaved all day to cook your meal. Moreover, your parents and grandparents who survived wars and the depression era may have made <u>you</u> eat more than you wanted because <u>they</u> feared there would never be another meal. Lastly, you may have learned to keep your body stuffed with food in order to stop yourself from expressing any and all of your unwanted emotions, thoughts, and dreams.

Hence, when it comes to eating and life in general, you need to be able to give yourself permission to <u>ignite your inner gauge</u> and to say to others:

- 'No'
- 'No more'
- 'No thank you'
- 'I don't want any more'
- 'I've had enough for now'
- 'I'm filled up'
- 'I'm full/satisfied/satiated'

In addition to being physically full, you and your inner child also want to be fulfilled or satisfied with the work/career you do, the relationships you are in, and all of your outside hobbies and activities.

When your relationships and career are richly rewarding and satisfying, they help to fill up your heart and soul. And when they are not, you may seek solace by filling yourself up with your beloved favorite foods instead.

We all truly yearn to be involved in activities and to be around people—family, co-workers, bosses, friends—that fill us up versus tear us down, let us down, and wear us down.

Furthermore, when you lessen your food intake and calories on a diet, you may be running on empty to make it across the weight loss finish line. And if you are already running on empty or merely running low on love and attention, you could feel like giving up even if your diet has only just begun. Maybe you've only got only a few pounds to lose, yet it may seem like you'll have to run a marathon to get into the slender body you desire.

To boot, the diet foods you choose to eat may lack flavor, taste, and richness when compared to the beloved favorite foods (and other foods) you are used to eating. Not to mention that a lifetime of back-to-back dieting feels like constant deprivation.

Your Weight Loss Discovery Journey makes it easier to bring to light all that you are starving for, hungry for, and longing for in your life.

A part of your being knows that you want and need to be nourished with love, attention, and all the other non-food forms of soul fuel mentioned in the 'Sweetness' chapter; yet food is so readily available that we use it as a substitute. Partly because we learned that food equals love and attention—and, partly because others in our lives may not give us much of either one.

Give yourself permission now to discover and give voice to what you may find unfulfilling in your life. Doing so will let you and your inner child to do two things:

- Be better able to gauge when your physical body is filled up with food; and
- Allow you to fill up your heart and soul with other, non-food things that you find satisfying and rewarding.

Your Weight Loss Discovery Journal: FULLNESS

For the following journal opportunities, write down what first comes to mind. And if nothing comes to mind, allow your inner child to use her imagination creatively.

1. What do you find unfulfilling in your relationships with others and/or your career?

EXAMPLE: I find the following things unfulfilling in my relationships and/or my career...

2. Write down 3 (or more) non-food related things that you find rewarding, satisfying, or fulfilling in your life.

EXAMPLE: The things that I find rewarding, satisfying, or fulfilling in my life are...

24

LOVE

Love Makes The World Go Around

Love made our little world go round when we were children.

We thrived in all sorts of circumstances when we were showered with unconditional love and its six counterparts—adoration, affection, attention, acceptance, appreciation, and acknowledgment.

The love we received made us feel special, cared for, and safe in the world and allowed us to relax in the deepest part of our being. It also permitted us to love ourselves—quirks and all—and provided us with a healthy foundation of self-love, the beginnings of healthy self-esteem and self-acceptance.

To this day, we may still long to be loved by our parents or caregivers, as well as by our spouses/significant others. We even want the love that can be found in friendships, with pets, and in nature. We may also long for our fellow humans around the globe to love each other and themselves and bring an end to hate, fear, revenge, violence, and wars that surface when love is missing or absent.

If we didn't get enough unconditional love growing up, we may now be left waiting and weighting for love to come to us, especially from our parents. We may still be trying to prove to them that we are worth our weight in gold. Not just any gold, but the finest gold—24 karat.

To earn love, we've tried so long and hard to become the good little girl—to be as good as gold—with our behavior, accomplishments, careers, and romantic relationships. Yet, the love we seek may not be forthcoming; or it may be fleeting when it does arrive.

Love truly makes the world go round and makes life more enjoyable when people treat us lovingly. When we are loved or in love, everything feels good, light, hopeful. Yet, when we aren't loved unconditionally or love gets taken away, our little world can come crashing and tumbling down around us—and can send us immediately into the pit of despair.

We depend on external sources of love for our emotional survival. When we receive unconditional love, it plants a fire firmly in our hearts. That kind of love provides a light that is always shining within the heart of your inner child—a pilot light in the furnace of your soul that never goes out. This fire within your heart and soul still blazes brightly. Even during your darkest moments, it always illuminates your path in life through intuition, insights, and inner guidance you receive.

You may have only been given unconditional love when you were a helpless little baby, when you were sick, or when you got hurt. Or not.

Consequently, you may have learned a variety of behaviors, such as acting out, acting in, being passive-aggressive, or buttering someone up to get the love and attention you wanted and needed.

If you didn't get unconditional love, attention, and time from others, you learned to accept them with conditions—sometimes going against your own inner truth to do so. You may have settled for tough love or substitute tokens—foods, gifts, gadgets, toys, clothes, and money. You may have even given those to yourself as a form of reward and self-love, adding drugs, prescriptions, and other altering substances and creating nothing less than a toxic love potion.

You may have also learned to accept unhealthy forms of attention to get the love you needed, especially in romantic relationships. You may have equated sexual advances and intimacy with love—sometimes selling yourself short to get your fix. After all, love is like a drug for your soul, for it makes you feel high; and to get by in life, you and your inner child need regular doses of it (albeit the healthy kind).

On some level, you may be starving for love.

If you suffered from multiple pains and disappointments like most of us did, a part of your heart may have shut down a long time ago. Or at the very least, you may have put up an energetic barrier around your heart.

You may now find yourself at odds with parts of yourself, afraid that your heart may never fully open to let love in. This leaves you feeling half alive and is compounded by the fear of never being able to love anyone else ever again.

Lots of love songs tell us all about what to expect from love—from it stinking to it being a many splendored thing.

Love is what we are after, and if no one else is dishing it out on a gold or silver platter, we may give ourselves a food substitute in place of the real McCoy. You may stuff and gorge yourself full of food—and other substances—until you feel that you've had enough love in these substitute forms. You may even unconsciously keep extra pounds on your body to brace yourself for all the tough times that you know lie ahead—even if it hurts your body, health, and well-being to do so.

We all so desperately want to be loved and to be seated at the table of love's banquet. Yet, our quest for love can sometimes feel more like the search for the Holy Grail—elusive or hard to get a hold of. Oftentimes this leaves you and your inner child looking for love in all of the wrong places—starting with the fridge or pantry/cupboard to see where love is hiding from you.

Dieting serves to remind us of all the things we are not allowed to have. Plus, it removes our beloved favorite foods from the table once again. We may eat a lot of good, healthy, and nutritious foods on a diet, yet still feel as if we are being punished until we can finally prove our worth to others. What we are really trying to prove to others is that we are worthy of being loved; yet in the meantime, we can spend our days trying to love ourselves close to death with food instead.

Love is a form of prayer that helps feed and fill the heart of your inner child. As corny as it sounds, it truly is the answer to the majority of what's eating at you and weighing parts of you and your body down.

Your Weight Loss Discovery Journey is taking you on a voyage back into the center of your precious heart and giving you the keys to let you and your inner child back into it. Because when it comes to losing weight and keeping it off for good, it's not really about the food.

Acknowledging that your relationship with food is complicated and related to more than just the quantity or quality of what you put in your mouth allows you to easily and safely give yourself permission to reopen the door to self-healing and self-love.

For the following journal opportunities, write down what first comes to mind. And if nothing comes to mind, allow your inner child to use her imagination creatively.

1. How did you try to earn the love of your parents and caregivers growing up?

EXAMPLE: To earn the love of my parents and caregivers growing up, I tried the following things...

2. List 3 (or more) people or non-food related activities/things that you love.

EXAMPLE: I love the following people, activities, things...

25
ENJOYMENT

Licking Your Chops

You can really sink your teeth into something you enjoy that gives you pleasure—be it food, a hobby, a good book, a movie, or a performance of any kind.

These joyful pastimes light you up from the inside and leave you grinning from ear to ear. They also rekindle the enthusiasm you felt for life when you were a kid and were happy and giddy for no apparent reason that adults could understand.

We really got a charge out of a lot of what we did as kids—playing with toys and board games or letting our imaginations run wild with make-believe.

We could play for hours totally in the zone, immersed in our own little world. Whether we were playing alone or with others, we were totally unaware of the day passing—unable to hear or defiantly ignoring the cries to come eat or just to come in out of the dark.

We were able to live off the ether that the universe had running through our lungs, veins, and arteries. The secret code name for this ether was happiness—the laughing gas for the soul.

Yet now all we may get as an adult is a 30-minute happy hour or some relief/enjoyment when we watch our favorite TV program or eat our beloved favorite foods. And we'll milk those for all they're worth.

Life got so serious somewhere along the way that enjoyment, enthusiasm, and excitement are now optional and only available to us after our daily work is done or we are on vacation.

You likely feel there is not enough real fun or play in your adult life—no playtime, no create time, no fun time, no laughter time, no relax time, and no down time—think nap time. ☺

We became fully an adult when we stopped doing things for the fun of it and started doing it for the funds—literally turning our fun and games into funds and gains.

A few of us are fortunate enough to have turned a childhood dream/passion, artist or athletic talent, or creative endeavor into our life's work and livelihood. Yet the majority of us are stuck working for the man or the woman in order to put bread on our tables and clothes on our backs.

As adults, we may spend our days in meetings, shuffling papers, returning calls and emails, managing other people's schedules, meeting deadlines, and working late just to get everything done and keep our jobs. And if you work at home, your day may include all that plus cooking, cleaning, shopping, and helping everyone else get all of their work done.

In either of those worlds, there may never really be a moment's rest or opportunity to kick up your feet and chill out, let alone live spontaneously.

And being on a diet means cutting out the fun and enjoyment as you cut back on calories and give your favorite nibbles the pink slip. A diet means no longer living in joy, but living in deprivation, restriction, and control. And definitely no more rewarding yourself with foods that give you enjoyment.

Yes, you already know that being on another diet means delaying gratification and enjoyment one more time.

That's why on a diet, you'll be left salivating and licking your chops watching others eat, yet you'll have to wait to indulge in your food fantasies until after you cross the weight loss finish line. Or, you always have the option to cheat on your diet and treat yourself...even if it's for the briefest of moments to enjoy some foods that tickle your fancy, especially if you'd prefer not to wait until you reach your weight loss goals.

After all, delayed gratification isn't all it's cracked up to be.

Other areas of your life that bring you enjoyment are also impacted when you go on diet, and this may add to any levels of frustration or isolation you may already be feeling.

Working to get in better shape may force you to give up your free time in order to exercise or shop and prepare foods on the diet menu. You may also choose to pass up on happy hour and other social gatherings just to avoid the temptation that goes along with these events. In doing so, you also miss out on the good times and laughs you may have gotten to share with friends, co-workers, and loved ones.

By continuing to do the writing exercises in Your Weight Loss Discovery Journal, you give yourself the opportunity to discover a different way to relate to food by uncovering and bringing into the light all the things weighing you down. This in turn allows you and your inner child to heal your relationship with food, so you can bring back your enjoyment in food and life for good.

For the following journal opportunities, write down what first comes to mind. And if nothing comes to mind, allow your inner child to use her imagination creatively.

1. What don't you enjoy about exercising or working out?

EXAMPLE: I don't enjoy the following things about exercising or working out...

2. Write down your favorite toys, games, and hobbies you enjoyed as a kid.

EXAMPLE: The favorite toys, games, and hobbies that I enjoyed as a kid were...

26

<u>LETTING GO</u>

Release What You're Holding On To

A deep exhale, sudden emotional outburst, or really good cry can sometimes make you feel lighter and freer—as if the sheer force of grace has lifted a great burden from your shoulders.

Letting go of things you've been holding on to for days or decades can provide you with a deep release at the inner core of your very being.

What you hold on to is sacred to you.

You may hold on and choose to not let go of all the pain caused by the wrongs, disappointments, betrayals, and broken promises of others. As mentioned in the 'Pain' chapter, the people who caused your pains may not be in your life or even among the living, yet some part of you may not be ready to let go.

You may hold on to things from the past and resist letting go because you are waiting for people to follow through on their promises, weighting for someone to apologize and say they're sorry, or wanting someone to kiss your ache and make it feel better so it will finally go away. And you may choose to consciously forgive those who inflicted the pain, yet never really allow yourself to forget.

Letting go can be extremely challenging because we learned to control our emotions by stuffing them down into our bodies. These compacted hurts are also active in the recesses of our minds as memories that are continuously shuffled and replayed, even when we sleep.

Now, when these trapped emotions are triggered by others in your life—others who may be totally innocent—it's as if the original painful events are happening again, for the very first time.

The icing on the cake for many of us was being made to apologize to parents, authority figures, and others when we did nothing wrong.

We were also told to accept another's apology and forgive them, even if we were not ready to do so.

Our earliest encounters with these sorts of scenarios occurred at the playground/in the sandbox with bullies/troublemakers and when we stood up or spoke back to anyone in authority.

We may have felt that our hands were tied because of this. Consequently, we may have held on to a lot of deep-seated anger and resentment that has built up over the years for all that we were told to apologize for.

For many, the only way to survive is to harbor a grudge and harden our hearts, closing them off to others. This makes our physical bodies carry the weight of those grudges and energetic burdens.

We may even want others who caused us pain to experience pain and suffer as we did—and consciously and unconsciously wish them ill or imagine how we could get back at them. We may never follow through on any of it, yet we may derive a sense of satisfaction from the repressed anger fantasies that play out in our minds. And if we brew poisonous thoughts, we are attacking our own minds and bodies, as well as harming our physical health and emotional well-being.

Holding on is like walking around with clenched hands all of the time. It is a form of control as well as a form of self-protection. You may use holding on as a way to control others by reminding them of what they did, manipulating them, or forcing them to acknowledge your existence. Or you may hold on to pain as a reminder not to trust others or let your guard down again. This keeps you safe and your heart protected from any further hurt and disappointment.

You may be afraid to let go and express all that you've been holding in and holding on to—afraid the dam will burst open if you do. You may also fear that letting go or surrendering may feel like a defeat, or worse, like an acknowledgment that the other person has won and still gets to be in control.

Letting go is not a defeat. It is a victory.

A triumph of heart and soul over the mind—a mind that tries to retain control by holding on to worn-out, painful memories that manifest as physical weight and pain in your body.

There may be many other problems in your life that you'd also like to let go. Maybe you'd like to let go of stuff on your overwhelming to-do lists. You may also long to let go of the grief for all of your losses, especially of your loved ones or for things you didn't get that you'd been hoping, wishing, and praying for. And if you're currently on a diet, you might also wish to let go of controlling yourself around food, so you can eat what you'd like and still have the pounds come off for good.

However, the only time you may truly feel comfortable letting go of feeling so controlled is when you are on a diet and choose to treat yourself to your beloved favorite foods—or when you choose to indulge in other addictions or get a rush from extreme sports (as already mentioned in the 'Control' chapter).

On a diet, as with most things in life, you are not supposed to let go of controlling yourself. You may even think that your current weight, a.k.a. 'letting your figure go', is the end result of your not being able to control yourself. Yet, throughout Your Weight Loss

Discovery Journey, you're discovering everything that is weighing you down—physically, mentally, emotionally, and spiritually.

Whatever you are holding on to, it would do your body good to contemplate looking at how it has impacted your whole life. Could you let it go? Even if you don't know yet, would you at least be willing to free yourself and let it go? Are you ready to be gentler and kinder to yourself and your body? Are you willing to start forgiving yourself?

The paradox is that more you hold on to something that weighs heavy on you emotionally and mentally, the more weighed down your body can become physically as a consequence. You may have been aware of the former, yet not the latter.

Letting go would be the antithesis of control. Yet, a lifetime of controlling ourselves, controlling others, and being controlled by others seems hard to let go of.

Letting go would allow you to relax and enjoy yourself, as well as liberate and free your mind, your heart, and the rest of your body, including your excess pounds.

No one can force you to let go of what you are holding on to. Yet when you start to become gentler on yourself and your inner child, the pressure that's been building up behind the floodgates begins to lessen. You also give yourself permission to forgive yourself and your inner child for merely trying to survive on a daily basis.

This internal letting go will become more organic the more you practice. Your heart will soften and you will begin to free yourself up energetically. By letting go of the things that have weighed you down, your pounds will more naturally be released from the inside out.

Be gentle with yourself at first. You may need to take baby steps with letting go, because it's a muscle that has atrophied, yet can be built up again. Try to practice with small things, like others being late, you being stuck in traffic, the weather forecast—try to let go of trying to control those outcomes and situations.

When you consciously choose to let go of something, you empower yourself. You also free your body and soul from the weight of anxiety that is caused by holding on.

Letting go is a way for you to respond to situations in the present, instead of simply reacting in a knee-jerk way as you have done in the past.

The opposite of letting go is to retain. And oddly enough, when the weight won't budge after years of dieting, it is worth taking a moment to reflect on all that you are holding on to.

This process is the key to liberation and freedom.

In addition to doing the exercises at the end of every chapter, give yourself permission to energetically release what you're holding on to by writing down everything you want to say—hold nothing back—and then imagine putting it into a balloon and watching it drift off into the vast sky above you.

For the following journal opportunities, write down what first comes to mind. And if nothing comes to mind, allow your inner child to use her imagination creatively.

1. What do you wish you could let go of that you've been holding on to for a long time?

EXAMPLE: I wish I could let go of the following things that I've been holding on to for a long time...

2. List 3 (or more) non-food related things that help you to unwind and let go of your worries.

EXAMPLE: The things that help me to unwind and let go of my worries are...

27

SOCIAL EATING

Putting You On the Spot

Social gatherings of any kind where two or more people have gathered together—at home, at school, at work—can be a blast or they can be laced with anxiety. They can begin well and end badly and vice versa.

You carry with you all of your positive and negative experiences from every previous social gathering with family, friends, peers, co-workers, classmates, significant others, and complete strangers.

If you've had more positive experiences, you may naturally look forward to social gatherings. Yet, if you've ever had a bad experience where someone put you on the spot or embarrassed you, you may dread those upcoming events or situations. You may also have embarrassed yourself as well with something you said or did.

At social gatherings, you may be looking to relax and unwind. Or you may be expecting to meet a romantic partner, business associate, or friend. On the other hand, you may be looking to avoid someone whom you are not interested in or disagree with, especially if you know that person will be at the same social gathering. You may also become anxious about running into rude or angry people, a gossip, or anyone who drinks too much and then says or does obnoxious things.

You know who those people are.

In a social setting, all of your self-worth issues rise to the surface and you may doubt your intelligence, humor, looks, or social status. You may even begin to question whether you're any fun to be around. You may feel insecure and worried that you have nothing interesting to talk about, particularly when meeting people for the first time. If you don't know what to say, it's sometimes easier to just listen, especially if you feel uncomfortable, awkward, or intimidated by others. However, if you don't participate in the conversation, it may feel like you are eavesdropping and then it becomes harder and harder to join in, and even harder to find an excuse to slip away altogether.

The whole event may leave you feeling like a deer caught in the headlights.

Hence, when you are around others at social gatherings, you may choose to comfort yourself with food and drink to help lower your anxiety. You may opt to keep your hands and mouth full whether you are standing or seated.

Keeping your hands occupied while standing can create a physical barrier and stop you from having to connect in ways that might make you feel uncomfortable. It's also a great way to avoid physical contact with others. The same goes for keeping your mouth full in order to stop yourself from speaking.

We all get more self-conscious in the public eye with or without food in the mix. Part of us feels this way because it reminds of us of childhood times when we were made fun of, cut off, invalidated, laughed at, shamed, blamed, punished, shunned, or completely ignored by others.

Now as an adult in any social setting, you may very well feel like you are diving into a whirlpool full of sharks and stingrays. Hence, your survival mode kicks in and gets your adrenaline running—just in case you should need to swim away from the situation.

If you show up to a work-related gathering full of co-workers and bosses, you could bite down on any residual anger, resentment, or jealousy that may be percolating from receiving an unflattering performance review, getting passed over for a promotion, or not getting a bonus or raise. If you feel owed in any way, you may choose to gorge on all the free food and drink available at these types of company functions. Or, if you are on the company's dime, then you may max out your expense account at your favorite restaurants.

When you are out with friends, you may not want to eat differently than everyone else—which makes being on a diet very challenging. You may just go along with everything and not make a fuss, scolding yourself the whole time. You also may resent having to deprive yourself while everyone else is enjoying the meal or choose to make an exception just this once.

You may be able to bypass all sorts of food temptations at home, yet when you are out in public, the temptation can seem amplified. Surrounded by all sorts of yummy delights, you may convince yourself to make an exception. Or, you may choose to reward yourself if you've been really good on your diet. Or, you may just want to treat yourself after a hard day and indulge in everything.

Also, at social gatherings with family, others may get offended if you don't eat what's offered. They may even fill your plates and glasses—still serving you like a helpless little kid and treating you as though you have no say in what you want or don't want. Plus, your family members expect you to play the role you've always played to keep the peace and not draw attention to yourself. You may also feel compelled to stuff down your anger and any other emotions at these gatherings as well.

All these things feed off each other in social settings and you can end up feeling like you have no control over anything.

Hence, when unwanted emotions are triggered and brought to the surface in any social setting, you may reach for food and be unable to stop yourself from shoveling it all in. With all of those emotions trapped inside of you, it's no wonder your waistline inflates like a balloon. You may very well stuff yourself to the point of being sick and uncomfortable the rest of the night.

Trying to stuff down your unwanted emotions and feelings is really the main factor contributing to your social overeating.

If there is alcohol at any of the events, you may find yourself drinking more than usual to relax and enjoy yourself, especially when stress and anxiety levels ramp up or if you've been under a lot of pressure.

However, inhibitions disappear as alcohol, narcotics, and the effects of sweets and other simple carbs begin to take effect. And that's why a little too much alcohol can open the floodgates of all that you have tried to suppress, leaving you vulnerable to behavior that can make you feel embarrassed or mortified.

Smartphones and social media make any missteps even worse since photographs or gossip can be instantly transmitted worldwide. We can also use our gadgets as a way to block others from having conversations with us or to keep people at arm's length; yet if you are the one who is on the receiving end of that at a gathering, you will likely feel ignored, invalidated, or invisible. As a result, you may seek out your beloved favorite foods and drink to keep you company.

Regardless of whether or not you are on a diet, you run the food gauntlet every time you attend a social gathering that involves food and drink. This is intensified during the holiday season which has its official kick-off with Halloween candy. The fun and frolic continues until January 1st or January 2nd when you re-commit to your diet and make this the year you finally shed all of those extra pounds you've been carrying around with you for so long. Yet, the first week of January often comes and goes with promising to start your diet tomorrow, yet tomorrow never really comes.

Before you subject you and your inner child to another diet, utilize Your Weight Loss Discovery Journey to discover why social settings make you so anxious in the first place. Doing so will allow you to begin to forgive yourself for trying to comfort and protect yourself with food at those occasions.

For the following journal opportunities, write down what first comes to mind. And if nothing comes to mind, allow your inner child to use her imagination creatively.

1. What makes you nervous or anxious about social gatherings?

EXAMPLE: The following things make me nervous or anxious about social gatherings...

2. Write down 3 (or more) non-food related activities that you enjoy doing with your co-workers and friends.

EXAMPLE: I enjoy the following non-food related activities with my co-workers and friends...

This is your final friendly reminder to return to any previous chapter in the book and finish the written exercises in the sections you have not yet completed in Your Weight Loss Discovery Journal.

'Getting To The Heart Of The Platter' helps you leave the land of dieting and say goodbye to years of constantly fluctuating between retaining weight that won't budge or regaining weight you've already lost.

The writing portion of these exercises lets you and your inner child acknowledge what you are truly starving for.

This acknowledgment then becomes the catalyst that allows you to achieve your ideal weight and to maintain it.

You can start right now. ☺

Return to any chapter and give your inner child back her voice, so the pounds finally come off for good!

28

TREAT

Contents Fragile: Handle With Care

The way you were treated growing up influences how you allow others to treat you and how you treat yourself today with or without food.

We all want to be loved; after all, it's our birthright. We also long to be treated with respect, dignity, and acceptance—and to be handled with the utmost care as if we were the most precious gem/jewel on the planet—a one-of-a-kind.

We'd all like to have the red carpet rolled out for us and to be treated like a VVIP—Very, Very Important Person. What's more, we want all the benefits in the Bill of Rights and the Declaration of Independence—personal freedoms, as well as life, liberty, and the pursuit of happiness. Which, to many of us, means being thin.

Unfortunately, others, especially your parents, may have made you feel unworthy or completely ignored you to assert their control. They may even have mistreated you in a variety of ways, especially with food. Now when your fragile/delicate heart aches or is hurt, you may unconsciously feel the need to treat and comfort yourself with food because you often used it as a pain reliever in your childhood. You may also take something stronger to numb the hurt and pain, including alcohol, over-the-counter or prescription medication, or illegal substances.

In addition, you probably learned to associate treats with behaving well, excelling in school and sports, or helping you feel better when you were upset or sick. So now when you feel you've been good or need a pick-me-up or pat on the back, you treat yourself to your favorite things—chocolate, candy, cakes, ice cream, bread, chips, carbs—especially if there is no one else around to comfort you or acknowledge all of your hard work and accomplishments.

If you've been incredibly good on your diet, you may still want to treat yourself. Yet, if you believe you only deserve a treat every once in a while or on special occasions, consuming your food of choice becomes a guilty pleasure—whether you are on a diet or not. You get to enjoy your treat in the moment of consumption, yet then feel a level of guilt for giving into it. Even though eating in and of itself is a pleasurable treat—just thinking about certain food can make people feel guilty. That sort of guilt can weigh you down and wear you out in the process.

That's why the multi-billion dollar food and diet industries make tons of money letting you treat yourself with a low-fat, low-calorie version of what you really want.

Those industries create advertising to hit all of your emotional triggers, so you will consume their smartly packaged products that will never fill you up or make you feel whole inside your heart—where it hurts the most.

Since food is addicting, you always need the next serving of comfort or pleasure to get that high or numb out. And once you've reached the bottom of the bag, emptied the container, or finished off the pint or half-gallon, you reach for the next...and the next...hoping to find love weighting for you at the bottom.

Your self-treatment with food may be a cry from deep within your soul—a cry to be treated to a real serving of love and then another real serving of love...and another...and another until the void in your heart is filled up and you can be freed from reaching for foods as a way to heal the ache felt there.

Prior to being on Your Weight Loss Discovery Journey, no amount of willpower would have been able to eclipse the hurt of your inner child who needed and wanted to be comforted in those aching moments.

We all pretty much have our issues with food due to all of the mixed-messages we received growing up. Plus, no one really ever gave us the tools/know-how to handle and to heal our emotions. So when your suppressed and unwanted emotions get triggered, it can lead to overeating your beloved favorite treats.

Your reaction to unwanted feelings can then become a vicious cycle of "trigger, treat, guilt" which may lead you to a diet where you deprive/restrict/control yourself. That is, until the next time you "trigger, treat, guilt" yourself.

Luckily, Your Weight Loss Discovery Journey is helping you to recognize how you've been treating yourself with food to make up for how you and your inner child may have felt you were mistreated by others growing up and now.

Bringing these sorts of issues into the light of day allows them to be transformed and empowers you to declare your wants and needs to others—including yourself—so that, starting today, you can have a freer and more relaxed relationship around food.

Your Weight Loss Discovery Journal: TREAT

For the following journal opportunities, write down what first comes to mind. And if nothing comes to mind, allow your inner child to use her imagination creatively.

1. Who did you feel ignored by growing up and whom do you feel ignored by now?

EXAMPLE: I feel I have been ignored by the following people in my life...

2. List 3 (or more) emotions you feel safe and comfortable expressing.

EXAMPLE: The emotions I feel safe and comfortable expressing are...

29

GUILT

Pouring On The Guilt

Guilt feels like something overflowing within you. It floods your mind and your conscience, drowning your soul in its toxicity.

Guilt weighs heavy and keeps you and your inner child shut out of your own heart. It squashes self-pride, self-esteem, and self-worth and replaces them with self-reproach, regret, and remorse.

The guilt you carry around with you makes your physical body feel heavy—a heaviness that you can't quite shake. What contributes to that feeling is that we've all been raised to feel guilty for merely having thoughts about something and then for acting on our thoughts. Hence, guilt can feel more like a two-fold ball and chain punishment—one for thinking and two for doing.

On a diet, you may feel guilty for merely fantasizing about food and in particular, your beloved favorite foods—especially if you believe that you'll eventually cave in and enjoy yourself. Which then results in another serving of guilt for cheating on your diet. And even if you are not on a diet, you may still feel guilty just thinking about certain foods and eating anything that you believe will make you gain weight.

These guilt-ridden scenarios are further intensified if you were punished or shamed with food in any way growing up.

If only all of our guilty pleasures related to the foods we eat came with guilt-free calories, then we might finally be able to eat whatever we wanted and simultaneously achieve the body of our dreams.

In addition to all of the guilt you have regarding food, you may even feel guilty for standing up for yourself or choosing yourself first over another. You may also feel guilty about having needs and wants in the first place or wanting them to be fulfilled by others, especially your need for time, love, and attention.

You may even feel guilty for not exercising or taking better care of yourself.

Guilt has its origins in our childhood when we were shamed, blamed, and punished for gazillions of things. And as talked about in the 'Letting Go' chapter, you may have also been made to apologize for things you didn't do, as well as forced to forgive others even if you didn't want to.

You and your inner child had to walk the line and pay lip service to the adults in your life in order to keep the peace and avoid further punishment.

We mainly got shamed and punished as innocent little children for doing what kids are supposed to do—exploring our worlds and venturing outside of the 'My Way or the Highway' thinking. And we were always promptly guilt-tripped right back to where others needed and wanted us to be—under their control and within the confines of their structures and belief systems.

And if those in authority over you did their jobs well enough, you eventually learned to self-police, self-reproach, and self-shame—which only serves to keep dragging you back to the old 'My Way or the Highway' rigid beliefs others have about what is right and wrong.

It's quite normal and okay to veer off the path—that's what exploring, trailblazing, and finding your bliss are all about. Yet the guilt you may feel for doing so reminds you of all the bad or wrong choices you or others believe you've made—further proof of your inherent unworthiness, shameworthiness, and blameworthiness—all imposed on you by others. Because of how your caregivers and those in society raised and punished you, you probably continue to shame, blame, and control yourself, as pointed out earlier in the 'Control' chapter.

Guilt is a form of control imposed on you by others, because if others can make you feel guilty, they can then control you. Those others then claim to hold the key to release you from your guilt by choosing whether or not <u>they</u> will forgive you.

You may have even been told that you are not worthy of being forgiven—now or ever. Consequently, you do not realize that you have the power to forgive yourself, especially when and if no one else will.

Self-forgiveness is like an energetic muscle in your body that needs to be stretched and worked out, the same as your physical muscles. It's closely related to the 'Letting Go' muscle and similarly, we aren't really sure about how to go about forgiving ourselves. Yet, we could sure use the practice of ceasing to drown in our guilt and to safely remove the wall around our hearts and lovingly come back into our own good graces.

It truly does your body, mind, and soul good to let go and erase the guilt and regret you've been carrying with you from one place to another, especially as it relates to food and eating. And, when you learn to forgive yourself, you begin to easily and safely lift the heavy burdens weighing you down that your heart has been energetically forced to hold within you. Doing so then allows self-love back in the heart of your inner child who needs and deserves as much love as you are willing to give her.

You and your inner child are truly worth forgiving yourselves.

You may very well have a good cry just thinking about being allowed to forgive yourself. The end result of all of this is that you begin to lighten up, which helps to prevent others from being able to control you so easily since you'll be immune to their efforts as they attempt to pour on the guilt.

We are human. We will all make mistakes. In spite of that, you will hopefully learn and grow, so you can avoid having to repeat them. Seeing how your actions and words impact others, as well as yourself, helps you more easily let go of any guilt and regrets.

And when you unburden yourself through the exercises that are found in Your Weight Loss Discovery Journal sections, you will begin to create a healthier relationship with food that you can easily maintain, which in turn then allows you to joyfully enjoy foods you love.

'Out beyond ideas of wrong-doing and right-doing
there is a field.
I'll meet you there.'
~Rumi

<u>Your Weight Loss Discovery Journal</u>: GUILT

For the following journal opportunities, write down what first comes to mind. And if nothing comes to mind, allow your inner child to use her imagination creatively.

1. What do you wish you could forgive yourself for?

EXAMPLE: I wish I could forgive myself for the following things...

2. Describe the best vacation or trip you've ever had. Or, describe the vacation of your dreams.

EXAMPLE: The best vacation or trip I've ever had or want to go on is filled with the following things...

30
OTHERS FIRST

On The Lifeboat Of Life

Others first is the last chapter in 'Getting To The Heart Of The Platter' so you can consider putting others last—or at least put yourself before many other people in your life.

You could benefit immensely from letting this idea percolate in your body, mind, and soul for a few days because the habitual mindset of others first isn't serving your health or your waistline.

We all were trained in society to be pleasing and self-sacrificing for the good of everyone else—our families, our schools, our employers, our social networks, and even the country we all live in.

Over the years, you became highly skilled at deferring to other's wants, wishes, and desires. As a result, you learned to sacrifice many of your own wants, needs, and dreams for all of those tribes—to show your dedication, love, respect, and allegiance.

At one point, you may have even been asked to swear your loyalty to any or all of them; and in return, you may have gotten sustenance, protection, an education, or a paycheck. You may have also gotten the love, attention, acceptance, and approval you'd been seeking, albeit sometimes at a cost of going against your own inner truth.

You learned in the 'Support' chapter that as a woman, you've been consciously and unconsciously conditioned to put others first in life through watching your mother and other women do just that. Consequently, we go on automatic pilot when other people are around and we go out of our way to make sure their needs are met first and foremost—and maybe that is one of the main reasons the human species has been able to survive for so long.

At this point in your life, you've put others first so often that it may be hard for you to receive the same kind of support from them. You may even feel uncomfortable giving to yourself at all, even after you've given to everyone else. Plus, you may have also reached a point in your life where you don't expect anything from anyone else, convincing yourself that if you don't hold the world together for everyone else, who will?

However, it may be easier for you to stay focused on everyone else as a way to avoid dealing with what bothers you or is truly weighing you down.

Even this far into Your Weight Loss Discovery Journey, you may not really be ready to delve deep and may use your focus on others as an excuse to keep yourself too busy to focus on and resolve your own issues. Regardless, know that wherever you are in this moment is perfectly okay.

Doing for others, giving them care, and showering them with attention may mean you love them. You may express this love through the foods you make. Or rearranging your schedule or sacrificing what little free time you may have just to make sure they get to all of their appointments, events, business functions, play-dates, and parties. If you work outside of the home, you may take time off when others are sick to nurse them back to health.

You may do for others to make and keep people happy which in turn may make your life easier in the short run; yet this choice puts excessive pressure on you to never let the ball drop. This also creates endless hours of unnecessary anxiety as you try to gauge or control everyone's mood or second-guess what they truly want.

You may do for others first because of the power struggles that you experience with your spouse, significant other, or other people in your life. These individuals may be quite demanding of your time and attention, and you may feel powerless or guilty if you serve yourself first.

And when you do everything for everyone else, it's inevitable that more and more gets shoveled onto your plate. Your repressed anger and resentment levels may rise when others, who are fully capable of doing the simplest of things, now expect you to do them.

The more you do for others, the more your own health, well-being, wants, and desires are out of your reach. If you could only wave a magic wand and get others to step up, fully take care of themselves, or do their own work, then you could devote more of your time to getting your body back in shape by exercising, cooking, and preparing foods that serve you.

Doing things for others can really put you in a bind if you use it to control others or to exert your power. You may also do for others as a way to prove your value to them. For if you are in control of everything, you become indispensable. Yet unconsciously making others dependent on you may bite you in the end. Serving others first may actually work for awhile until rebel forces choose to remove you as their dictator—for no one really likes to be controlled, let alone told what to do.

You could benefit tremendously by learning to give to yourself first. Try to think of it like the safety message the flight attendant gives before each flight: You need to put your oxygen mask on first, so that you will be better able to assist others.

Just like the 'Letting Go' and 'Self-Forgiveness' muscles, serving 'Yourself First' is another energetic muscle that once flexed can help you to breathe easier and shed unwanted pounds in a more relaxed state of mind.

Having made it to the end of this book is proof to you and your inner child that you are looking for a weigh out of the weight loss conundrum you've been living in for years.

Take a moment now to honor and congratulate yourself for being willing to go on Your Weight Loss Discovery Journey in the first place. Because you were willing to read and complete each chapter, you actually did put yourself first! This allows you to heal parts of your inner child that have ached for years.

The toughest part of the journey is over.

You have now truly given yourself permission to heal at your deepest core, so that in the long run, you will be able to keep the pounds off for good!

Your Weight Loss Discovery Journal: OTHERS FIRST

For the following journal opportunities, write down what first comes to mind. And if nothing comes to mind, allow your inner child to use her imagination creatively.

1. In your daily life, whose needs and wants get satisfied before yours?

EXAMPLE: The following people's needs and wants get satisfied before mine...

2. Write down 3 (or more) opportunities in your daily life to serve yourself first.

EXAMPLE: I could serve myself first by...

AM In-Joyment

Celebrate Your Success!

And the crowd goes wild!!!

Take a moment to truly celebrate you and your inner child crossing the finish line of

Your Weight Loss Discovery Journey!

You stayed the course and identified many self-defeating behaviors and ideas you had about yourself, dieting, and your relationship to food in general.

This is a major, life-altering accomplishment that provides freedom from food controlling your life!

Relish this moment.

As places that have been hidden and hurting continue to come into the light of day or as new events unfold, feel free to go back to any previous chapter's journal section and do the exercises found there.

To download a pdf file containing the questions in each chapter to make it easier for you to complete them, go to http://gtthotp.com/handouts/gtthotp%20questions.pdf

If you feel inspired to continue to keep a journal, remember to include your inner child and to use your imagination creatively.

And let me be the first to encourage you to take pleasure in all the non-food related activities you can to help fill up your heart and soul.

Be kind and tender with yourself—every day—in all areas of your life and especially with your relationship with food! And whether or not you choose to follow any specific diet plan, you will now be more capable of nourishing your body and soul in healthier ways.

To your continued in-joyment and weight loss success!

'Keep knocking and the joy inside will eventually
open a window
And look to see who's there.'
~Rumi

Appendix: Positive Feelings

Accepted
Accomplished
Acknowledged
Authentic

Blissful
Bold
Brave
Brilliant

Calm
Capable
Centered
Cheerful
Cherished
Clear
Comfortable
Comforted
Committed
Compassionate
Confident
Connected
Content
Courageous

Delighted
Determined
Devoted

Eager
Easy-going
Ecstatic
Effective

Elated
Empowered
Enchanted
Encouraged
Energetic
Enjoyment
Enthusiastic
Excited
Exhilarated

Fascinated
Focused
Forgiving
Fortunate
Free
Fulfilled
Full

Generous
Gifted
Glad
Grateful
Great
Grounded
Guided

Happy
Healthy
Honored
Hopeful
Humorous

Ignited

Inspired
Integrated

Joyful

Kind

Light
Lively
Love
Loved
Loving

Magical
Majestic
Motivated
Mystical

Open
Optimistic

Patient
Peaceful
Permitted
Phenomenal
Playful
Pleased
Positive
Powerful
Present
Protected
Proud

Radiant

Refreshed

Relaxed

Relieved

Renewed

Respected

Respectful

Responsible

Rewarded

Safe

Satiated

Satisfied

Secure

Seen

Settled

Spiritual

Special

Successful

Supported

Surprised

Sweet

Sympathetic

Tenacious

Thrilled

Tranquil

Triumphant

Trusting

Unstoppable

Understood

Validated

Valued

Victorious

Visible

Vital

Whole

Worthy

Youthful

Appendix: Negative Feelings

Abused	Devastated	Hurt
Afraid	Diminished	
Agony	Disappointed	Ignored
Alienated	Disbelief	Impatient
Alone	Discouraged	Infuriated
Angry	Distracted	Insignificant
Annihilated	Doomed	Intimidated
Annoyed	Doubtful	Invalidated
Anxious	Drained	Irritated
Apprehensive		Isolated
Ashamed	Embarrassed	
	Empty	Jealous
Betrayed	Envious	
Bitter	Exhausted	Lifeless
Blamed	Exploited	Lonely
Bored	Exposed	Lost
Bothered		
Bummed	Fatigued	Mad
	Fearful	Miserable
Cautious	Fed Up	Mortified
Challenged	Frustrated	
Cheated	Furious	Negative
Condemned		Neglected
Confronted	Grief	Nervous
Confused	Guilty	
Controlled		Outraged
Crippled	Hateful	Overwhelmed
Crushed	Heartbroken	Panicked
	Heavy	Pitied
Dead	Helpless	
Defeated	Hesitant	Rage
Depressed	Hopeless	Regret
Destroyed	Humiliated	Rejected

Remorse
Resentful
Responsible
Restless

Sad
Scared
Self-hatred
Shocked
Shut-down
Skeptical
Sorrowful
Stopped

Struggling
Stunned

Teary
Tense
Terrified
Threatened
Torn
Trapped

Unable
Uncomfortable
Undermined

Unsure
Upset
Used
Useless
Unsupported

Vulnerable

Weak
Withdrawn
Worried

Want some additional support?

Or just looking to build your support team/cheering squad?

If so, consider participating in the online version of this book which is called EasyGoingWeightLoss.com.

This internet-based program has all the same great chapters as in this book and incorporates EFT (Emotional Freedom Techniques®) into each of the journaling exercises.

EFT is an easy-to-learn, easy-to-use, fast-acting, self-applied acupressure tapping technique which helps to bring about immediate shifts in your energy, so you can quickly overcome your personal barriers to success.

This online program might be right for you if you want to:

- Feel further supported and empowered on Your Weight Loss Discovery Journey
- Create a healthier relationship with food you can easily maintain
- Feel more energetic
- Connect with other women on the same journey
- Heal core issues stressing you out or emotionally weighing you down.

To participate or to simply learn more about the benefits and details of this program, go to: http://easygoingweightloss.com/

Weighting To Be Rescued Off Dieter's Island

Cynthia Magg

Adrift in a Sea of Emotions, you find your lifeboat drifting closer and closer towards the excesses of Temptation Island—which is the last place you want to end up when starting a brand new diet.

Only a few days into the plan and you're already struggling to stay the course amid continuous emotional waves that threaten to capsize your efforts.

Things can go south pretty quickly when you simply and impulsively reach for your beloved favorite foods to keep those emotional waves calmed. For this reason, south of your own equator (a.k.a. your waistline), you already bear the evidence of this kind of overindulgence—on your hips, thighs, and backside.

Totally exhausted after days of mentally paddling away from temptation (or years, considering how many other diets you may have been on), you're not exactly sure what happened after you fell asleep on your dieting watch/vigil. You just know that somewhere in the middle of the night you went overboard and raided the fridge—only to find yourself washed ashore on an even more formidable location called Dieter's Island.

Alone, out in the middle of nowhere, and feeling punished, you wonder how you'll ever be able to escape from being on a Dessertless Island Eating Twigs, or if you'll be trapped here for the rest of your life trying to become one of the thin people.

You pinch yourself and hope it's just a nightmare—yet this is real!

Coming Winter 2013

Stay Tuned!

This book is a bedtime story for you and your inner child—to fill up your souls with a little humor, wit, and wordplay while you contemplate the world of dieting.

It is a lot lighter and easier to digest
than the heavy book you've just finished reading,
'Getting To The Heart Of The Platter'.

This upcoming book is written from my inner child to yours. ☺
Enjoy!

Cynthia

Kitchen Help, Farmers, and Other Sunshine

'What I was hiding deep inside,
You brought out into the light.'
~Rumi

Christina Alex and Rebecca Ortese—Thank you both for your awesome editing! You both truly have a gift with words and made writing this book more enjoyable.

Victoria Song—All I can say is thank you for picking up the phone on more than one occasion when I found myself in the pit of despair. My soul is eternally grateful to you. Namaste.

Gary Craig—A heartfelt thanks to you though I have never met you. Your Emotional Freedom Techniques® has allowed me to heal multiple things in my own life.

Tania Massamiri—I appreciate you helping me reframe my thinking around many issues I found so challenging in the moment. Thank you for the message you conveyed to me to 'Write, write, write'. Mahalo.

'Help Find the Typos' team—Gillian Baggen, Rabinder Singh, Christina Alex, and Rebecca Ortese—Your keen sets of eyes were truly all a blessing. Thank you!

Lee Glickstein—Thank you for your wonderful Speaking Circles® support groups which allowed me to reconnect with my true inner speaker. I feel so much more relaxed speaking in public because of your work. Blessings to you.

Clients—Thank you for allowing me into your life. You all really have hearts of gold and are truly courageous! Wishing you all continued healing from the inside out.

Previous employers—Thanks to all of you for providing me with a paycheck.

My family of origin—Thanks for hosting my soul in this life. I wish you all peace.

Friends →Gillian: Am so glad you showed up at the Ritz kitchen all those years ago and am grateful for all the times we had tea and other visits. Glad I still get to see you (and Lindsay) on Skype to help bridge the distances. Thanks for your friendship and support. →Christina: Thanks for goofing around and exploring things East and West. Looking forward to more wacky adventures. Thanks for your friendship and your cheerleading/WOM (Word Of Mouth) to others on my behalf. →Suzie: Thanks for encouraging me to get into health/healing work and for helping me get my business started by sending me clients! And thanks for all of the road trips, readings, shared meals, and laughs. Here's to the energy shifting in this lifetime for good! Thanks for your friendship. →The boys: Thanks for letting me be a part of your life growing up. It was an honor. →Inky: Thanks for being the friend who drove all those miles to support me on my vision for athletes. Looking forward to more belly laughing and finally sitting in a sweat lodge. Fire horses unite! Gam Sa Ham Ni Da. →Little bear: You were definitely an angel sent to me in my hour of need in Paris. Thanks for helping me reconnect to the places in me that are still young at heart. Merci. →Lesley: What can I say other than gelato, chocolate, hiking, and lots of laughs, eh! What else are friends to share? →Oldies yet goodies: To the friends in MA, PA, PR, NJ, CO, CA, NY, and Canada. I thank all of you for all the laughs, the times we've had together, and for your support. I wish you all peace and joy.

<u>Team Divinity</u>—Thank you muses, angels, light bearers, goddesses, and gods for all of your guidance, support, and signs that show up everywhere in my life. ☺

'Love is the energizing elixir of the universe,
The cause and effect of all harmonies.'
~Rumi

About the Chef—author—who cooked up this book!

Cynthia Magg is the founder and owner of TranscendingMindset.com, an organization which empowers people to overcome internal barriers to success, so they can more easily achieve their goals and get what they want. Formerly a financial analyst, pastry chef, and homeopath, she now is a Goal Fulfillment Accelerator who teaches easy-to-learn transformational techniques to individuals and groups. She has worked with moms, athletes, actors, writers, lawyers, executives, and other busy people who seek to enrich their lives and reclaim their health and well-being. She also coaches men and children. She lives in the San Francisco Bay area.